DEVELOPING SHAPE, SPACE & MEASURES
WITH 5-7 YEAR OLDS

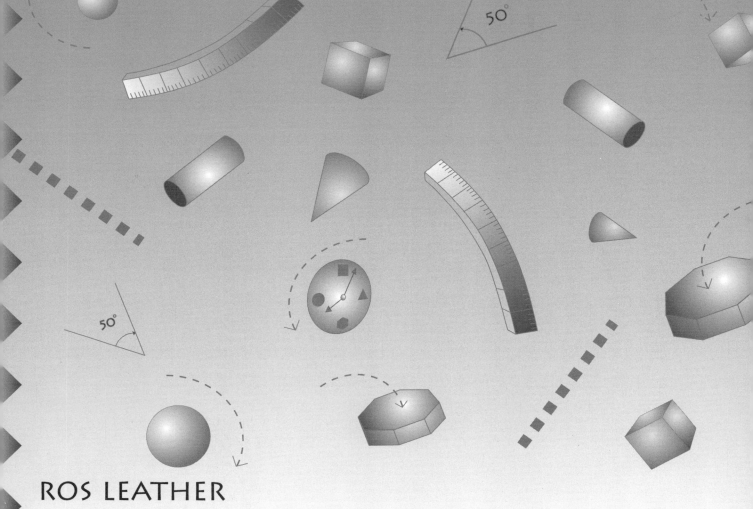

ROS LEATHER

Published by Scholastic Ltd
Villiers House
Clarendon Avenue
Leamington Spa
Warwickshire CV32 5PR

Text © 2000 Ros Leather
© 2000 Scholastic Ltd

1 2 3 4 5 6 7 8 9 0   0 1 2 3 4 5 6 7 8 9

AUTHOR
Ros Leather

SERIES CONSULTANT
Jon Kurta

EDITOR
Joel Lane

ASSISTANT EDITOR
Marian Reeve
David Sandford

SERIES DESIGNERS
Anna Oliwa and Sarah Rock

DESIGNER
Sarah Rock

ILLUSTRATIONS
Frances Jordan

COVER ARTWORK
Mark Oliver at Illustration

Designed using Adobe Pagemaker

British Library Cataloguing-in-Publication Data
A catalogue record for this book is available from the British Library.

ISBN 0-439-01773-4

CONTENTS

MEASURES

ABOUT THE AUTHOR

Ros Leather is Deputy Headteacher at Bishop Carpenter School near Banbury, where she manages and teaches the early years children. Over the last ten years, she has written for a number of educational publishers.

hen asked what constitutes the content of mathematics in the primary school, many people will think solely of arithmetical calculation. This part of the curriculum has been emphasized in the contemporary concern with standards that has led to the development of the National Numeracy Strategy *Framework for Teaching Mathematics* (March 1999) and the introduction of the 'daily mathematics lesson'. However, it is interesting that in the international studies that provoked such concern (such as the TIMMS study), British children actually performed well in comparison to their peers in spatial topics. This perhaps reflects the strong tradition in British primary schools of work on shape, space and measures – a tradition that embraces the Montessori philosophy, as well as Piagetian notions of 'learning through experience', and which has often involved

the innovative use of a range of practical materials (geoboards, geostrips, Poleidoblocs and others).

In children's everyday experiences, spatial encounters precede numerical ones. In the pre-school years, children are curious about their environment and keen to become familiar with the look and feel of everything around them. A young child picking up and pulling objects could be estimating their size and weight, as well as exploring the relationship between these attributes. As they learn to speak, children develop appropriate language to help them articulate their developing spatial awareness. Taken a step further, we can see how spatial awareness is as important as numerical awareness in many professions – for example, building, carpentry and clothing design.

This book provides activities that acknowledge sound practice in the teaching of shape, space and measures, but also aim to embrace contemporary issues. Particular emphasis is given to visualising

aspects of the topics, and to the role of language – both in the sense of accurate use and understanding of 'technical' vocabulary and in the sense of being aware of talk and discussion as an important mode of learning.

SHAPE AND SPACE
DEVELOPING VOCABULARY

SCAA's review of the 1996 Key Stage 2 SATs suggested that teachers needed to place more emphasis on the use of correct mathematical vocabulary for geometric shapes. It is not uncommon to hear children (and adults) referring to a ball as 'circle-shaped' and a box as 'square'. This misconception needs to be addressed, not glossed over. Typical misconceptions that occur in this area are well documented in the OFSTED Research Report*, and many are addressed directly in activities in this book. For example, research shows that children are less likely to recognize and name correctly shapes that are shown obliquely or that are irregular.

WORKING MENTALLY

The difficulties outlined also highlight the importance of talk and discussion. I may know what 'parallel lines' means, and I can close my eyes and picture them, but without dialogue it is unclear whether a group of children have the same mental picture. Spatial activities clearly need to involve a mental element as well as a physical one, and the ability to visualize objects spatially is important in everyday adult life.

It can also be argued that visualizing in spatial activities will be useful for children's development in mental calculation. For example, realizing that the subtraction 82 – 78 is best done by adding on from 78 may be helped by picturing the position of the numbers on a number line. Other examples include 'knowing' and using the dot patterns on a dice to recognize numbers and understanding how multiplication can be modelled with 'arrays' that link directly to area:

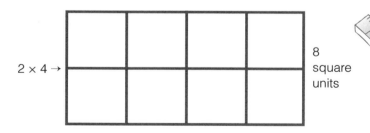

$2 \times 4 \rightarrow$ 8 square units

In the development of algebraic thinking, the use of patterns that combine a spatial element with a numerical element is also common practice. For example, the 'growing L' image is a visual way of representing odd numbers:

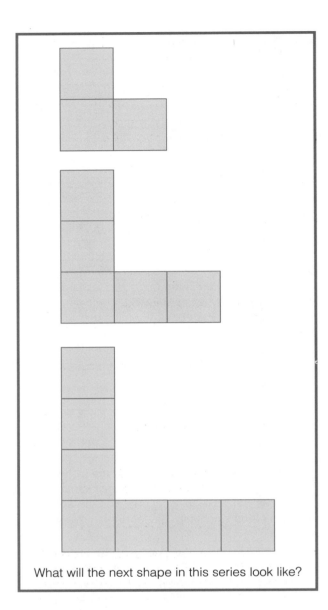

What will the next shape in this series look like?

MEASURES

Work on measures in primary schools is often seen primarily as a context for developing number. While not ignoring this aspect, this book puts particular emphasis on conceptual understanding of measures. As with shape and space, the emphasis is on visualization and discussion. (Further activities on calculations with measures can be found in the companion Scholastic series *Developing Mental Maths* and *Practising Mental Maths*.)

It is important that the teaching of measures should include:

● *Developing a 'feel' for what is being measured and the right words to express it. This involves firstly linking known words to the appropriate measure (for example, **heavy** and **light** are related to weight, **full** and **empty** to capacity), and secondly having a sense of the relative sizes of different objects – Which is the heavier stone? Which cup holds the most?*

● *Being able to make 'common sense' estimates. In many real-life practical situations involving quantities, we do not need to know an exact measure: for example, when parking my car, putting milk in my coffee or buying a handful of vegetables, I only have an approximate idea of the length of available kerb, the volume of milk or the weight of the vegetables respectively. However, I am confident that I won't hit the car behind, overfill my cup of coffee or buy too many vegetables. It is important to help children build up this 'common sense' of different measures.*

● *Systems of units. Children need to know both the numerical relationships between units (such as 100cm = 1m) and their relative magnitude in practical use. For example, the length of a pencil is best measured in centimetres, but the distance across the playground is best measured in metres. It is important to build up children's images of the relative size of different units.*

SOLVING PROBLEMS

While learning about shape, space and measures, children need to be actively engaged in problem solving. This provides a purposeful context for the development of skills and an environment that fosters discussion. Talk needs to be skilfully led in order to make sure the children's attention is focused and misconceptions are addressed. It also provides a vehicle for assessment of the children's understanding.

Additionally, it is through talk that a shared understanding of particular vocabulary can be established. For example, the concept of 'perimeter' (see page 78) can be built up by talking about each side of an oblong, then the two pairs of equal sides, then the four sides.

ABOUT THIS BOOK

This book is split into two main sections: 'Shape and space' and 'Measures'. Each section starts with a double-page glossary (pages 8–9 and 72–73) which highlights relevant vocabulary, particularly where it is likely to be new to this age group. Each glossary can be enlarged for display as an A2 poster (copy each A4 page separately onto A3, then join them back together) or copied at normal size for desktop use.

The two main sections are divided into sub-sections dealing with particular topics. Each sub-section starts with a two-page spread, highlighting:

● **Key ideas.** *What the children need to know overall – the key concepts that need to be considered when planning a unit of work on this topic for the appropriate age group.*

● **Common misconceptions and difficulties.** *Key teaching points, many of which are emphasized in particular activities.*

● **What children should know by the end of Reception/Primary 1, Year 1/Primary 2 and Year 2/ Primary 3.** *This relates directly to the NNS* Framework for Teaching Mathematics, *the National Curriculum for England and Wales and the Scottish Guidelines for Maths 5–14.*

The activities presented in each sub-section fall into two categories: teacher-directed activities and group problem-solving. If you are following the National Numeracy Strategy, this division is well suited to the structure of the daily mathematics lesson.

The teacher-directed activities include ideas for introducing particular themes into whole-class discussion, including key questions which can be used for assessment. Some of these activities are short 'warm-ups' to use in the first part of the

mathematics lesson; others are suitable for extended discussion in a plenary session following group work on the theme.

The group problem-solving activities are intended to involve the children in group work, and include suggestions for different ability groups (though, as with number activities, this may not always be necessary).

Supporting photocopiable sheets provide either practice activities or resources. The practice activity sheets are designed to consolidate the main concepts. They also stimulate personal reflection or discussion by asking questions as indicated by the following icons:

 think (and be ready to talk) about it!

 discuss with your 'maths talk' partner

 tell your teacher

 write down [to help the children organize their ideas logically].

The use of these photocopiable sheets is intended to be flexible. A class can be split, with half doing a practical activity and the other half working on a practice sheet. The sheets can be used after the completion of practical activities; some may also be useful for homework or individual assessment.

A photocopiable writing frame is provided on page 128. This will help the children to reflect on their learning, and could be particularly useful when they have been engaged in practical or investigative work that has not left much recorded evidence. Activities for which the writing frame is particularly helpful are highlighted in the teachers' notes. The writing frame can be used directly as it is; alternatively, when the children have developed confidence in their writing about maths, they could use it as a basis for a freer account of their work. Asking children to write about maths is a good way to find out how confident they are in their grasp of mathematical vocabulary, and also how able they are to communicate their ideas – two aspects of mathematics which are important themes in this book.

*Askew, M. and Wiliam, D. (1995) *Recent Research in Mathematics Education* London: HMSO.

2-D SHAPES

circle
circular

curved

straight

triangle
triangular

*cor**ner***

oblong

side

square

flat

The oblong and square are in the **rectangle** shape family.

pentagon

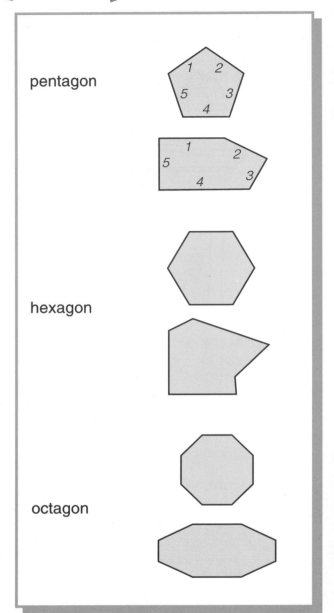

hexagon

octagon

POSITION & DIRECTION

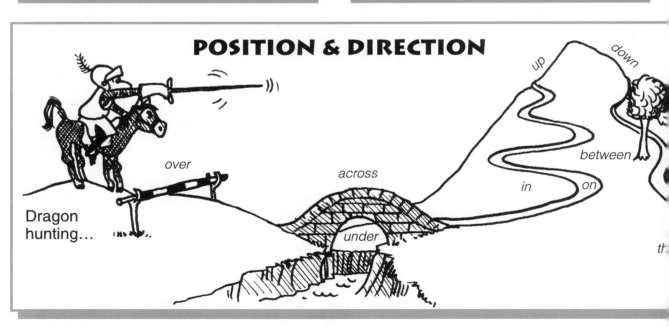

Dragon hunting…

over
across
under
up
down
between
in
on

3-D SHAPES

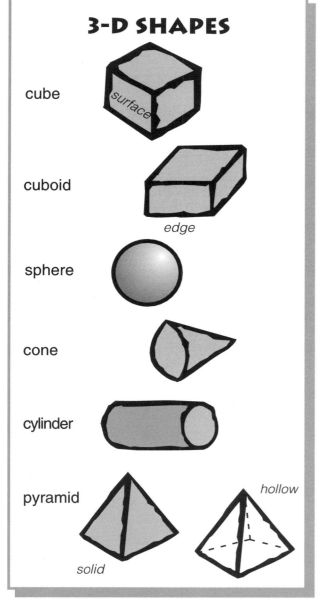

cube

cuboid

sphere

cone

cylinder

pyramid

surface

edge

hollow

solid

SYMMETRY

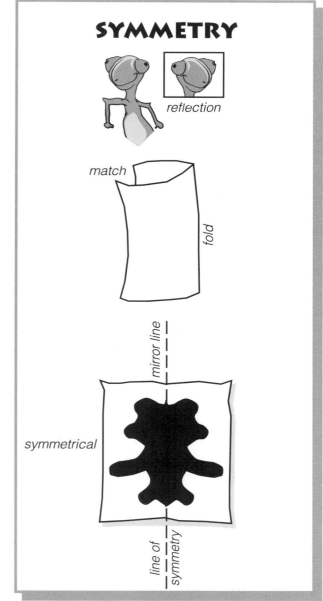

reflection

match

fold

mirror line

symmetrical

line of symmetry

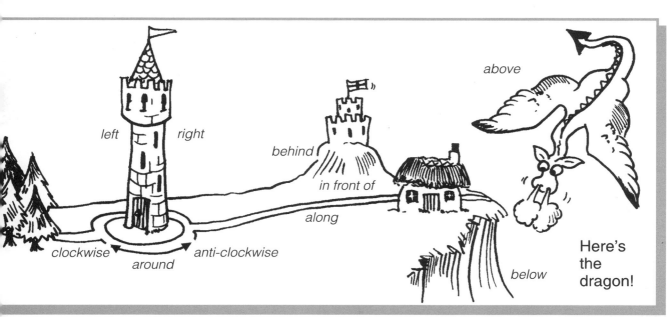

above

left   *right*

behind

in front of

along

clockwise   *anti-clockwise*

around

below

Here's the dragon!

KEY IDEAS

- Knowing the properties and names of common shapes.
- Recognizing shapes in a variety of orientations.
- Recognizing simple 2-D shapes on the faces of 3-D shapes.
- Knowing criteria to sort and classify a range of common shapes.
- Being able to combine shapes to make new ones.
- Understanding about basic tessellation (tiling patterns).
- Starting to visualize shapes (for example, in 'feely bag' activities).

Children need to be introduced to shapes from the beginning of their time at school. The majority of children are familiar with the common 2-D shape names when they start school. Unfortunately, they often use the 2-D shape names to describe 3-D shapes (as many adults do) – for example, calling a dice 'square' and a ball 'a circle'. This makes the teaching of shape more difficult, because the vocabulary used in school will frequently differ from (or even contradict) that used in the outside world.

Junk boxes are ideal for sorting and making models. Packaging is becoming increasingly diverse. It is always worth keeping unusual boxes and containers for 3-D shape activities. Although it is important to have a selection of commercial 3-D shapes in school, boxes have greater relevance and significance for children. Boxes can also be used to solve problems involving measures, such as: 'My box has ... faces. The faces are ... shapes. My box shape is called a .... My box is ... centimetres long, ... centimetres high and ... centimetres deep. My box balances with ... grams. Wayne has the longest box. It is ... centimetres long and measures ... centimetres more than my box.'

To make these boxes easier to paint and decorate, it will be helpful to turn them inside out. With adult help, the boxes can be taken apart at the seams, turned inside out and stuck together again. Use pegs to hold the seams together until the adhesive dries. It is best to allow one seam to dry before joining up the ends of the boxes. Having plain faces will make the 3-D shapes easier to sort and describe, as well as to decorate.

BY THE END OF R/P1 MOST CHILDREN SHOULD BE ABLE TO:

- identify and name simple 2-D and 3-D shapes in 'shape activities', around the classroom and in the wider environment, including 2-D faces on 3-D shapes
- make and describe 3-D models using words such as round, corner, triangle, square
- sort 2-D shapes by criteria such as 'square/ not a square'.

BY THE END OF Y1/P2 MOST CHILDREN SHOULD BE ABLE TO:

- begin to describe a wider range of 2-D and 3-D shapes using language such as corner, edge or face
- find a 2-D shape when given a description such as 'It has four sides of equal length'
- make models and patterns using regular templates for 2-D shapes and cubes or regular 3-D apparatus (eg, beads or building bricks)
- follow pictorial instructions to build 3-D models, eg, for using a simple construction kit.

BY THE END OF Y2/P3 MOST CHILDREN SHOULD BE ABLE TO:

- use language such as: circular, triangular and surface
- identify shapes such as pyramids and simple polygons
- choose an example to match given properties for 2-D and 3-D shapes, for example: 'I'm looking at a shape that has… corners and … faces. Which shape could it be?'
- progress to making models and patterns with more complex, composite shapes
- use straws etc to make 3-D skeletons and pinboards to make regular and irregular 2-D shapes
- use ICT to draw right-angled 2-D shapes.

SOME COMMON MISCONCEPTIONS

'THIN' AND 'THICK' SHAPES

A true 2-D shape is absolutely flat. It cannot be picked up, and it can only be represented by a drawing or a computer graphic. You will need thin card, plastic or laminated paper '2-D shapes' for practical work. These can be used to represent 2-D shapes, but are 'thin' rather than flat.

We live in a 3-D world, but most of our familiar shape vocabulary refers to a 2-D world: 'square', 'circle' and so on. To complicate matters, we often use 3-D shapes in school that we call 'thick' 2-D shapes. These are really 3-D shapes with their own names: cylinders, cuboids, prisms and so on (you may not want to use this vocabulary initially). Given the shapes shown below, instead of asking the children to find 'a circular shape', ask them to find 'a shape that has a circular face'.

OBLONGS AND SQUARES

The family of **quadrilateral** 2-D shapes is a very large one. At Key Stage 1/Primary 1–3, the children only need to know two of the shape names: **square** and **oblong/rectangle.** The National Numeracy Strategy uses 'rectangle' in the early years and only introduces 'oblong' in Year 4/Primary 5. Many children will come to school knowing the word **rectangle** to describe an oblong. However, the children will eventually need to know that a square is a 'special' rectangle (that is, a quadrilateral with four right angles), while an oblong is a quadrilateral with four right angles and with opposite sides that are the same length, but with one pair of sides longer than the other. This book consistently uses 'oblong' to avoid later confusion and reteaching, but you can substitute rectangle, of course.

Also, children will often refer to a shape (which is really an oblong) as 'squarish'.

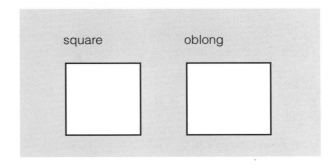

RIGHT WAY UP?

Children may find it difficult to recognize squares when these are shown at different orientations. Encourage them to turn a tilted square shape (or their heads) until they can recognize it more easily. Children will often refer to a square at an angle as a 'diamond'.

Many children (and their parents) only recognize a triangle if it is equilateral and has the apex at the top. It is important for children to be aware of other types of triangle (though they do not need to know their names) and recognize triangles shown at different orientations. They should recognize any shape with three straight sides and three corners as a triangle.

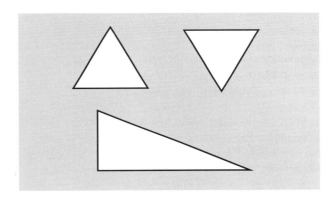

REGULAR AND IRREGULAR

From the outset, children should become familiar with regular and irregular shapes. As soon as they are familiar with regular pentagons, hexagons and octagons, they need to become aware that irregular versions of the same shapes are also called pentagons etc.

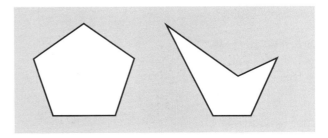

(sidebar) **2-D & 3-D SHAPES**

SORTING FLAT SHAPES

†† *Whole class, sitting in a circle*
⏱ *About 10 minutes*

AIMS

To sort 2-D shapes. To use appropriate shape vocabulary.

YOU WILL NEED

Thin card or plastic circles, squares, oblongs and triangles (preferably one colour per shape); four large pieces of paper cut into a square, a circle, a triangle and an oblong.

WHAT TO DO

Lay out the 2-D shapes in the centre of the circle of children. Explain that you want their help to sort these 'flat' shapes. Ask several children to choose a shape and place it in the correct group. Find out why they have chosen to place it on a particular paper shape. Encourage them to clarify their explanations, and to use suitable vocabulary to describe each shape.

DISCUSSION QUESTIONS

● *Who can find a 2-D shape to put on this [the circular] piece of paper?*
● *Why has Hassan placed his shape on this piece of paper? [Circles.]*
● *Who knows what this shape is called? Yes, it is a round shape and we call it a circle.*
● *Why has Megan put her shape on this paper? [Oblongs.]*
● *Who knows what her shape is called? Yes, we do sometimes call them rectangles, but a shape with two long sides and two short sides like this is called an oblong. [You may like to indicate that the paired sides are the same length, and are opposite each other.]*
● *How many corners does the circle have?*
● *What shape is the side of a circle? [Curved.]*
● *Do any other shapes in these sets have a curved side?*

ASSESSMENT

From the children's explanations, you will be able to assess how well they understand the criteria used to sort the 2-D shapes.

VARIATIONS

● Use 2-D shapes in a variety of sizes.
● Use 2-D triangles and oblongs that vary in shape (made from photocopiable pages 121 and 122): triangles not always equilateral, oblongs varying in their proportions.

EXTENSIONS

● Use set rings for sorting.
● Sort using other criteria: shapes with one, three or four sides; shapes with curved sides or straight sides.

NAME THAT 2-D SHAPE

†† *About 10 children, sitting in a horseshoe shape*
⏱ *About 10 minutes*

AIMS

To identify and name 2-D shapes. To use appropriate vocabulary to describe the shapes.

YOU WILL NEED

Card or plastic 2-D shapes (one per child); four large pieces of paper cut into a square, an oblong, a triangle and a circle, with the names of the shapes written on them; Blu-Tack or drawing pins.

WHAT TO DO

Pin or Blu-Tack the large paper shapes to the board one at a time, asking the children to name and describe each 2-D shape. You may need to remind them how to identify the shapes (for example: *Yes, it is a triangle because it has three straight sides and three corners.*)

Point to the words written on these shapes and read them in unison. The word **circle** may pose a problem: you may need to explain that in this word, you cannot hear the letter sound at the beginning. What you hear is the letter name (compare with **bicycle**, **ceiling** or **celery**).

My name is Mark and I am a hexagon.

Take down the sheets of paper and place them on the carpet with the card or plastic 2-D shapes. Ask the children to take a shape each. They should name the shape and say at least one thing about it, then place it on the appropriate sheet.

DISCUSSION QUESTIONS
● *What is your 2-D shape called, Emily? What can you say about your oblong?*
● *What can you tell me about your 2-D shape, Jack? Who else has a shape with four sides that are straight and the same length? Who can point to the word 'square'?*

ASSESSMENT
The children should be able to name the 2-D shapes. Many children may hesitate to describe the shape accurately; if so, it is important that an adult or another child extends the description.

VARIATIONS
● Vary the size of the shapes.
● Vary the shape (and orientation when placed on the floor) of the triangles and oblongs, using photocopiable pages 122 and 123 as sources of shapes.

EXTENSIONS
● Present the shape names on unshaped pieces of paper.
● Let the children use photocopiable page 22 to practise matching names to shapes.

WHAT'S IN THE BAG?

†† *About 8 children, sitting in a horseshoe shape*
🕐 *About 10 minutes*

AIM
To identify 2-D shapes from descriptions.

YOU WILL NEED
A cloth bag holding 2-D oblongs, squares, circles and triangles of various sizes (see photocopiable pages 120 and 121), large paper 2-D shapes (as above) with names written on.

WHAT TO DO
Pin up the large paper shapes at a convenient height for the children to reach. Let the children take turns to feel in the bag for a shape and describe it (without naming it). The child choosing a shape also chooses another child to point to the correct 2-D shape name and read it out before the shape is revealed. If the name is correct, he or she takes the next turn at describing a shape in the bag. Continue until everyone has had a turn.

DISCUSSION QUESTIONS
● *How did you know the shape being described was a circle?*
● *Which shapes are easier/harder to describe? Why?*
● *Why didn't we know which four-sided shape Abigail was describing?*
● *What else does Abigail need to say so that we are able to identify the correct 2-D shape?*

ASSESSMENT
Use the discussion questions to assess the children's ability to describe shapes and to identify shapes from descriptions.

EXTENSIONS
● Present the shape words on unshaped labels.
● Play the feely bag game with regular (and then irregular) pentagons, octagons and hexagons (photocopiable pages 124 and 125).
● To help the children develop their shape identification skills, let them complete photocopiable page 23. Emphasize that **any** five-sided shape is a pentagon, and so on.

2-D & 3-D SHAPES

2-D & 3-D SHAPES

BRICK BY BRICK

†† *Whole class, groups or individuals*
⏱ *Up to 1 hour*

AIM
To become familiar with 3-D shapes, particularly cubes and cuboids.

YOU WILL NEED
A friendly builder (optional), wooden bricks, a writing frame (photocopiable page 128); paper, pencils and colouring materials (optional).

WHAT TO DO
If you have an adult helper who can build, or there is construction work near the school, the children can see at first hand how walls are built, corners are made, spaces are left for doors and windows and so on. (Before visiting a building site, you should apply to the site foreman for permission.) A walk around the school can also stimulate discussion about shapes. Encourage the children to build structures using wooden bricks. Use their buildings to discuss the properties of different 3-D shapes.

DISCUSSION QUESTIONS
● *Which shapes are best for building walls?*
● *Can you describe how you made the bridge?*
● *Could you make the bridge longer? What would you need to do?*
● *Can you build with cylinders? How? Why do you need to balance the cylinder on a circular face?*
● *Who has made the tallest tower?*
● *Can you explain why Edward's tower fell down?*
● *Why do you think builders lay bricks horizontally?*

ASSESSMENT
Can the children show you how a builder turns corners with bricks?

BRING A BOX TO SCHOOL

†† *Whole class (or group) sitting in a circle*
⏱ *About 30 minutes*

AIMS
To sort 3-D shapes. To use appropriate vocabulary.

YOU WILL NEED
A box for each child (from home or school); five labels (**cube, cuboid, triangular prism, sphere, cylinder**) and wooden hoops. (You will need boxes in each 3-D shape – for example, a Toblerone box for a triangular prism.)

WHAT TO DO
Arrange the children in a circle, each child holding a box. Read the labels together and place one label in each hoop. Ask the children to count the faces on their boxes carefully, observing the shape of each face. They should take turns to describe their box and decide which hoop to put it in, focusing on the number and shapes of faces as the criteria for sorting.

DISCUSSION QUESTIONS
● *Has Raushan placed his container in the correct hoop? How do you know?*
● *Is this box a cube or a cuboid shape? How do you know?*
● *Which set has the most/fewest boxes in?*
● *Which containers slide/roll?*
● *Which containers could you use for building a model house?*

ASSESSMENT
● How confident are the children at naming the faces of their boxes?
● Can they describe their boxes?
● Can they read the 3-D shape labels?
● Can they extend their vocabulary to include the words **flat, curved, hollow** and **solid**?

EXTENSIONS
● Name a type of shape, then describe a box and ask all the children who think it belongs to that set to sit together. Ask: *Are all the boxes in this set the same? How do you know?*
● Look at some cuboid boxes and ask: *Do all of these cuboid boxes have six faces? Are all of the faces the same shape?* Encourage the children to see that some cuboids have only two square faces, and that some have none at all. They should be able to check whether a face is square or not by measuring the sides, using non-standard or standard units.

THICK OR THIN?

†† Whole class sitting in a horseshoe shape
⏱ About 30 minutes

AIMS
To sort 2-D from 3-D shapes. To describe the differences between them.

YOU WILL NEED
A selection of card or plastic 2-D shapes (very thin) and 3-D shapes, two set rings.

WHAT TO DO
Label the set rings '2-D' and '3-D'. Discuss with the class what the differences are between 2-D and 3-D shapes. Give each child or pair a shape. Ask the children to place their shapes in the correct set ring. Ask them to justify their choices.

DISCUSSION QUESTIONS
● *How did you know this shape [a narrow cylinder] was 3-D?*

ASSESSMENT
Are the children describing faces accurately? Can they justify their sorting (for example, by saying 'This shape is flat and very thin, so it is 2-D')?

EXTENSION
Provide relatively thin 3-D shapes (for example, flattened cuboids) and see whether the children can still identify them as 3-D. Explain that a true 2-D shape has no thickness at all.

MR TRIANGLE FACE

†† Half of the class
⏱ About 45 minutes

AIM
To identify 2-D shapes and use them to make a 3-D shape.

YOU WILL NEED
A shape with a triangular face, thin card, scissors, adhesive, self-adhesive labels, small card triangles, Polydron or Clixi.

WHAT TO DO
Show the children a triangular-based pyramid made from Polydron or Clixi. Pass it around the group and ask them to say something about it. You may need to write 'triangular pyramid' on the board. Ask the children to make the same shape using Polydron or Clixi. Ask individuals how they know that they have made a triangular pyramid. When they open out the shape and look at the net, what shape do they see? (See figure.)

Now use a shape with a triangular face to make the same net. Ask the children to help you draw round the shape. Where will the next triangle be drawn? Work together to draw the four triangles that make the net. Cut out the net and fold (or score) along each pencil line. Fold the net to make the pyramid and stick the edges together with self-adhesive labels.

Use smaller triangles to add facial features. Use strips of card with a tessellating triangle pattern for arms and legs. Attach triangles for hands and feet. You may want to make small triangular pyramids for hands, feet and a nose. Use wool, tissue or curled paper for hair; the children may suggest making a tessellating triangle pattern on the head.

Ask the children to design and make their own version of Mr or Mrs Triangle Face.

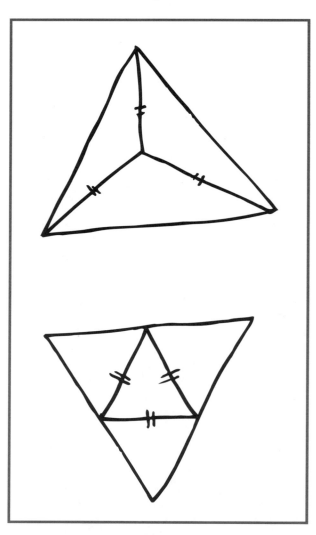

DISCUSSION QUESTIONS
● *How many triangles are there on his face?*
● *How many triangles are there on Mr Triangle Face altogether?*
● *How many triangles have you used to make his mouth? [Could be one or several.]*

ASSESSMENT
Observe how the children make their net: are they positioning the triangles to match the Polydron net?

EXTENSION
Adapt this idea to make dice, cuboid people or animals. Once children have mastered the basic principle, they are very inventive with their designs.

PINBOARD PENTAGONS

†† *Groups of 8 to 10 children*
🕐 *About 20 minutes*

AIM
To investigate the distinctive properties of some 2-D shapes.

YOU WILL NEED
A pinboard, elastic bands, a sheet of dotty paper, a ruler and a pencil for each child; 2-D pentagons (photocopiable pages 124 and 125).

WHAT TO DO
Hold up or draw a large pentagon on the chalkboard and ask:
● *What can you tell me about this shape?*
● *Who can describe the sides?... Are they straight or curved?*
Repeat with other pentagons (from pages 124 and 125), including irregular ones.

Ask the children to make a shape with five straight sides and five corners on their pinboards, then check with a partner. Do they agree that there is a pentagon on the pinboard?

Now ask the children to copy the shape they made onto dotty paper. You may need to enlarge the dotty paper sheet and demonstrate how to draw the pentagon accurately on it. Ask the children to design three more **different** pentagons and record them on the dotty paper.

DISCUSSION QUESTIONS
● *Are all your 2-D shapes pentagons?*
● *How do you know?*

ASSESSMENT
Check that the children are recording their shapes accurately on dotty paper. Ask them to say how two of their shapes are the same and how they are different.

EXTENSION
Use the same activity to explore triangles, quadrilaterals, hexagons and octagons. A photocopiable sheet of triangles is provided on page 122 (or the sheet of pinboards for making triangles on page 27 could be used).

WHAT IS MY SHAPE CALLED?

†† *A group of 8 children*
🕐 *About 10 minutes*

AIMS
To read 2-D shape labels. To match them to the correct shapes.

YOU WILL NEED
A set of seven cards labelled **triangle, square, oblong, circle, pentagon, hexagon** and **octagon**; a cloth bag containing card shapes to match these. (You may want to use shaped cards with children who find reading difficult, or who need a visual check. The labels on photocopiable page 126 can be copied and perhaps enlarged.)

WHAT TO DO
Deal out 2-D name cards to seven children. Ask the eighth child to feel and describe a shape in the bag. How quickly can the child holding the correct name identify the shape? These two children now swap roles. The group should play until each child has had at least two turns at describing a 2-D shape. You may need to make sure the children can read their labels before they play the game.

DISCUSSION QUESTIONS
● *Why was it hard to know which shape Sam was describing?*
● *Which shape is easiest/hardest to describe? Why?*

ASSESSMENT
Check whether the children are using appropriate shape vocabulary in their descriptions, and whether they can read the shape names.

EXTENSIONS
● Play the game with 14 children holding labels, including both regular and irregular 2-D shapes (named as 'irregular pentagon' and so on).
● Play with 3-D shapes, or a mixture of 2-D and 3-D shapes.

ALL SORTS OF SWEETS

†† *About 8 children*
🕐 *About 20 minutes*

AIM
To reinforce the characteristics and names of 3-D shapes.

YOU WILL NEED
Salt dough (prepared in advance, or with the children in a science lesson), a packet of liquorice allsorts, balances, standard or non-standard weights, paint and varnish.

WHAT TO DO
Session 1: Empty the packet of liquorice allsorts on the table. Ask the children to choose one each, describe its colours and then describe the shapes of its faces. The children should now make three sweet-sized balls of dough, each balancing with the same number of interlocking cubes. (If they are any larger than sweet size, they will be impossible to dry.) Ask them to make a cube, a (non-cubic) cuboid and a cylinder with their dough, then place them on a baking tray in a very slow oven until they have dried out completely.

Session 2: In an art lesson, ask the children to paint the sweets carefully in two or more colours. They may need to allow the sweets to dry between painting stages. When the sweets are dry, an adult can varnish them and then allow them to dry again. The sweets can be used for shape work or 'sold' in a class sweet shop.

DISCUSSION QUESTIONS
● *How many faces does your sweet have, Naayab?*
● *Does anyone have a sweet that will roll? What are these shapes called?*
● *Are all the cylinder sweets the same?*
● *How are they the same/different?*
● *How many faces does a cylinder sweet have?*
● *Are all the cuboids the same?*
● *How are they the same/different?*
● *Can you sort the sweets? [The children may choose to sort using criteria other than shape.]*

ASSESSMENT
Through discussion, assess the children's awareness of the properties of these 3-D shapes.

EXTENSION
The children could design new sweets using other shapes, such as triangular pyramids, square pyramids and cones.

2-D & 3-D SHAPES

MAKING A SHAPE MOBILE

⋔ About 10 children
(depending on age and ability)

🕐 About 45 minutes

AIM
To investigate the effects of halving and quartering shapes.

YOU WILL NEED
For each child: paper or thin card, a shape with a square face (a decimetre square is ideal), scissors, a pencil, thin strips of paper, adhesive.

WHAT TO DO
This activity could be carried out in the art area. Demonstrate it (either a stage at a time or in total) before the children make their own mobiles.

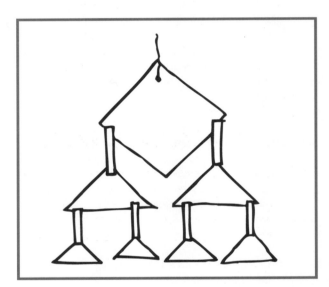

1. Draw round the shape with a square face three times, then cut them out. This stage can promote discussion about the best place to draw the shapes on the paper. Using the corners means less cutting and more economical use of paper.
2. Leave the first square complete. Fold the second square in half, either diagonally or vertically. Explain to the children that they need to be very careful. Once the shape is folded, ask:
● *How many shapes will I have when I cut along the fold?*
● *What shapes will they be?*
● *How do you know?*
Cut along the fold to make two oblongs (or triangles). Attach these with paper strips and adhesive to two corners of the first square (see figure above).

3. Fold the third square twice in the same way as the second square, then fold it again. Ask:
● *How many shapes will I have when I cut along the folds?*
● *What shapes will these be? [triangles, oblongs or squares]*
Open out the square, cut along the fold lines and attach the new shapes with paper strips and adhesive to the corners of the two shapes cut from the second square (see figure).
4. Attach a paper strip to the middle of the first square.
   Discuss the shapes in your mobile. Once the adhesive has dried, pin the mobile to the ceiling. Ask the children to make their own mobiles, perhaps working in pairs.

ASSESSMENT
As you observe the children making their models, individual assessments of their knowledge of shape can be made. Can they name and describe the shapes they are using? Ask:
● *When we folded our square twice, what shapes did we have?*
● *Did everyone have the same shapes?*
● *Why/why not?*

EXTENSIONS
● Try making mobiles with shapes not yet used: triangles or oblongs, or circles (using semi-circles and segments).
● If the children have used triangles, follow up the theme with photocopiable page 27.

CONSTRUCTION TIME

⋔ Whole class or group

🕐 Up to 1 hour

AIM
To become familiar with the 2-D shape faces of 3-D shapes.

YOU WILL NEED
Polydron or Clixi, a writing frame (photocopiable page 128); paper, pencils and colouring materials (optional).

WHAT TO DO
Interlocking shape kits such as Polydron and Clixi encourage children to make models by constructing and joining 3-D shapes – for example, making a cube or cuboid house with a square pyramid or rectangular prism roof. Encourage model-making in structured activities and free play, using discussion

to enhance the children's learning. Groups can be set tasks:

- *How many different pyramids can you make?*
- *Can you make a bigger triangular pyramid?*
- *How many different cuboids can you make?*
- *Make a cube, then take it apart to show the net.*
- *Join up six squares to make a flat shape.*
- *How many different 3-D models can you make using the same six pieces?*

Afterwards, ask the children to draw and write about their work: which shapes they used, how many of each shape they used, which shapes they couldn't use. They can use the writing frame on page 128. Choose individuals to tell the class about their models; encourage and praise the correct use of relevant vocabulary.

DISCUSSION QUESTIONS

- *How are these pyramids different?*
- *How many faces has your pyramid? [Some children will take it apart and count the pieces.] What shape are the faces?*
- *How do you know these cuboids are different?*
- *Has everyone made the same net for a cube? How are they the same/different? Will they all close up to make a cube?*
- *Which flat shapes will/will not fold up to make a cube? Why is that?*

ASSESSMENT

When the children show you a face, check that they are not pointing to the individual Polydron pieces.

EXTENSION

The children can use photocopiable pages 24–26 to explore different aspects of the 2-D faces of 3-D shapes.

A SHAPE PICTURE

†† *Half the class at a time*
🕐 *About 45 minutes*

AIM

To explore how 2-D shapes can be combined to make more complex shapes.

YOU WILL NEED

Sheets of coloured paper, a variety of 2-D shapes, pencils, adhesive, scissors, large sheets of plain paper.

WHAT TO DO

Take a large sheet of plain paper and ask the children to help you choose shapes to make a house. Ask them to place suitable 2-D shapes on the paper. Discuss their choices:

- *Will it be a house or a bungalow?*
- *What shape shall we use for the front of the house?*
- *How many windows will we need? What shape will they be? Can we have window-panes?*
- *Where will we put the door?*
- *What could we put in the garden?*

Ask the children to design their own picture by drawing round the shapes on coloured paper, cutting them out and sticking them onto plain paper.

DISCUSSION QUESTIONS

- *How many triangles have you used in your picture?*
- *Which shapes have you used to make the tree?*

ASSESSMENT

Check that the children are using the correct 2-D shape names when describing their pictures.

EXTENSIONS

- The children could design pictures using two types of 2-D shape only.
- They could write descriptions of their pictures, explaining which shapes they have used. Younger or less able children could tell an adult helper, who could scribe the description.

A JUNK MODEL

†† *About ten children (in pairs)*
🕐 *Two sessions of about 30 minutes*

AIM

To investigate how 3-D shapes can be used to make more complex models.

YOU WILL NEED

A collection of boxes (turned inside out for sticking and decorating), plastic containers and cardboard tubes; card, adhesive; materials for decoration.

WHAT TO DO

Ask the children to design a 3-D model using the boxes and containers. You may want an extra adult to help with holding the models together. Encourage the children to discuss their plans and ideas, focusing on one idea before starting their designs. Encourage planning before they start to stick things in place. Can they explain and justify their choices?

In a follow-up session, the children can decorate their models. Use this as an opportunity to reinforce their awareness of 3-D shapes.

DISCUSSION QUESTIONS

- *What shapes are the boxes you will use?*

2-D & 3-D SHAPES

- *Why have you chosen a cuboid with two square faces for the body of the car?*
- *What will you use for wheels?*
- *What shape will they be? [Cylinders.]*

ASSESSMENT

Are the children able to explain and justify their choice of shapes (for example, 'I needed four cylinders for wheels because they will roll')?

VARIATION

Choose a theme to stimulate the children's modelling, such as the flying machines in *The Giant Jam Sandwich* by John Vernon Lord and Janet Burroway (Pan).

CYLINDER CATS

†† *Half the class at a time*
🕐 *About 45 minutes*

AIMS

To identify and use the 2-D faces of a 3-D shape. To explore cylinders.

YOU WILL NEED

Paper, shapes with an oblong face, adhesive (or self-adhesive labels or staplers), pencils, scissors.

WHAT TO DO

Demonstrate how to draw round an oblong-faced shape and cut out the oblong. Ask the children whether you should make a fat or a thin cat. Curve the oblong to make a hollow cylinder; overlap the two straight edges and stick them together. Draw and cut out two triangular ears, two circular eyes, a triangular nose, narrow oblong whiskers and a spiral tail (made from a circle).

Ask the children to make their own fat or thin cats. Hang them up in groups, as mobiles, and use them for number work – for example: *How many groups of four are there? How many cats are left over? Why?*

DISCUSSION QUESTIONS

- *How can we make a hollow cylinder from an oblong piece of paper?*
- *Can you see another cylinder in the classroom?*
- *Can you build with cylinders? How?*
- *How many faces does a solid cylinder have?*

ASSESSMENT

Ask children to describe a cylinder. Can they show you how a cylinder can roll, and how they can build with cylinders.

VARIATION

The children could make Father Christmas cylinder mobiles, or use the shape to develop their own inventions.

EXTENSION

In a similar later session, the children can explore cones by making mice. They will need objects with a circular face (plates or lids) for templates. Show them how to make a semicircle by folding and cutting a circle, then curve over and attach the straight edge to make a cone. The more overlap, the thinner the mouse! Ears can be made from small semi-circles; eyes, whiskers and a tail can be made as for the cat. The mice can be displayed as a mobile. Encourage the children to be aware that a cone has a circular base. What other things have they seen that are cone-shaped?

AN EASTER BASKET

†† *Half the class*
🕐 *About 45 minutes*

AIM

To reinforce the 2-D shape faces of 3-D shapes by making 3-D shapes from 2-D shapes.

YOU WILL NEED

Thin card, two shapes with a square face (one larger than the other), scissors, pencils, small staplers (or adhesive or self-adhesive labels), rulers, gummed paper or tissue paper.

WHAT TO DO

Demonstrate how to make the basket (see figure). Draw round the larger square face and cut it out. Place the smaller square face in the middle of the large square and draw round it. Show the children how to extend each side of the smaller square to the edge of the outer square. Cut along these extension lines. Fold carefully along the pencil lines (or score with a scissor blade, if the children are old enough to do this) and staple or stick the card into a box shape. Cut out an oblong for the handle.

Ask the children to make and decorate their own baskets.

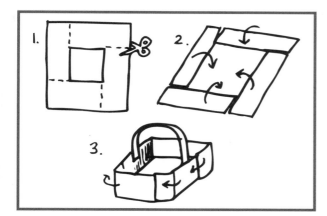

DISCUSSION QUESTIONS

● *Is this 3-D shape hollow or solid? How do you know?*
● *What shape is the base of your basket?*

ASSESSMENT

Discuss and question the children's knowledge of relevant 2-D and 3-D shape vocabulary.

EXTENSION

● The children can try using triangles, hexagons and oblongs to make baskets.

A TESSELLATING PATTERN

†† *Half the class at a time (in pairs)*
🕐 *About 45 minutes*

AIM

To investigate the tessellating properties of 2-D shapes.

YOU WILL NEED

Paper in several colours; objects with square, triangular or oblong faces; scissors, pencils, adhesive, plain paper.

WHAT TO DO

Choose a shape (for example, something with a triangular face). You will need two different-coloured sheets of paper (for example, red and yellow). Draw round the shape and cut out at least four from each colour. Stick one red triangle in the top right-hand corner of another large sheet of paper, leaving a small triangular space (see figure); this space can be filled later, using half of a yellow triangle.

Ask the children what you need to do to fit a red triangle next to the yellow triangle without leaving a space. Stick the red triangle in position and ask: *Which coloured triangle shall I use next to keep the pattern going? Who can put it in the correct place?* Ask different children to stick the remaining triangles in position to make a pattern of alternating colours.

The children can now work in pairs, using one shape and two colours to make their own tessellating patterns. If each pair make up a hexagon, all the hexagons can be combined to make a patchwork.

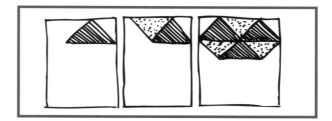

DISCUSSION QUESTIONS

● *Who can explain what 'tessellating' means?*
● *Do all our patterns tessellate?*
● *Could we use a shape that will not tessellate? What shapes do you think they could be? Why?*

ASSESSMENT

Note whether the children are able to make a tessellating pattern and to explain how their pattern was constructed.

VARIATIONS

● Provide shaped sponges for printing a tessellating pattern.
● The children can draw, then colour, a tessellating pattern.

EXTENSIONS

● The children can design more complex patterns from tiled pattern books, or from real examples in or near the school.
● They can use hexagons to make tessellation patterns.
● Use an OHP to project a large 'Elmer the Patchwork Elephant' shape onto a large sheet of paper on the board; the children can paint in his squared skin. (The *Elmer* books are by David McKee, published by Red Fox.)

GIVE IT A NAME

■ Write the name of each shape from the list below.

> triangle
> square
> oblong
> circle

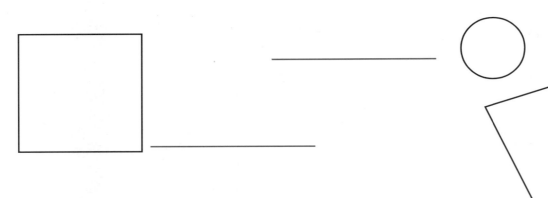

 Which shapes have **four** right angles? Tell a friend.

SEE 'NAME THAT 2-D SHAPE', PAGE 13.

HOW MANY SIDES?

■ Write the number of sides in each shape. Two shapes
have been done for you.

✏ Which ones did you just know?

😀 Which are hard to count? Why? Tell a friend.

SEE 'WHAT'S IN THE BAG?', PAGE 13.

**DEVELOPING SHAPE,
SPACE & MEASURES**

2-D & 3-D SHAPES

NAMES OF 3-D SHAPES

■ Colour the **cuboids** red, the **cones** green, the **cylinders** blue and the **pyramids** yellow.

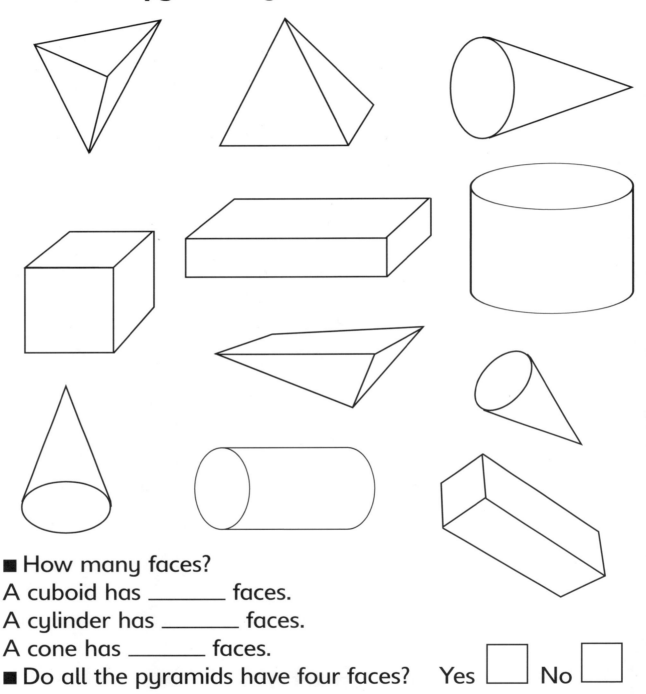

■ How many faces?

A cuboid has _____ faces.

A cylinder has _____ faces.

A cone has _____ faces.

■ Do all the pyramids have four faces?   Yes ☐ No ☐

 Which of these 3-D shapes will roll? Tell a friend.

2-D & 3-D SHAPES

2-D FACES ON 3-D SHAPES

■ Write the 2-D shape names of the faces by each 3-D shape. The first one has been done for you.

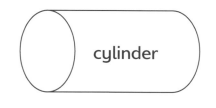

cylinder

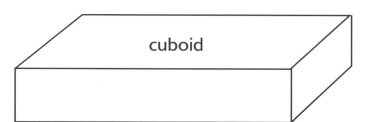

cuboid

_____

_____

2 circles
_____

1 oblong
_____

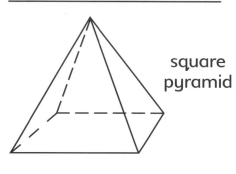

square
pyramid

cuboid

_____

_____

_____

_____

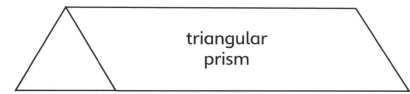

triangular
prism

_____

_____

■ Colour any 3-D shapes with five faces red.
■ Colour any 3-D shapes with six faces yellow.

 Which shape has two flat faces and one curved face? Tell the teacher.

SEE 'CONSTRUCTION TIME', PAGE 18.

DEVELOPING SHAPE,
SPACE & MEASURES

NAME _____   DATE _____

2-D FACES

■ Which 3-D shapes can you make with these faces?

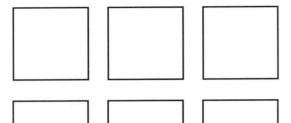

I can make a _____

I can make a _____

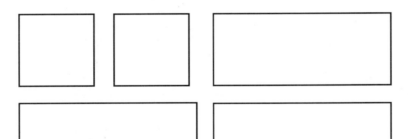

I can make a _____

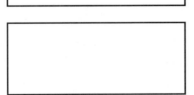

 Try making these shapes from Polydron. Tell a friend how you did it.

SEE 'CONSTRUCTION TIME', PAGE 18.

PINBOARD TRIANGLES

Join the dots to make a different-shaped triangle on each board. One has been made for you.

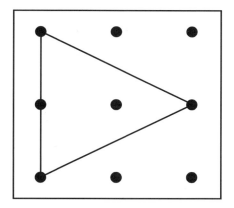 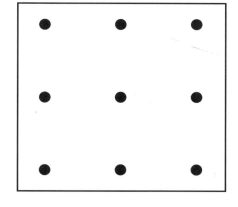

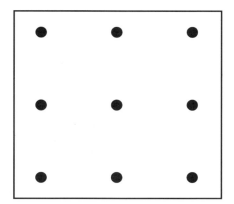 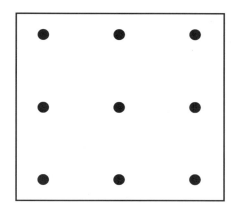

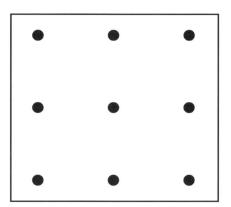 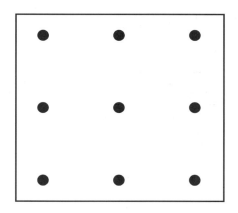

 Tell a friend how your triangles are different.

SEE 'PINBOARD PENTAGONS', PAGE 16; 'MAKING A SHAPE MOBILE', PAGE 18.

DEVELOPING SHAPE,
SPACE & MEASURES

2-D & 3-D SHAPES

KEY IDEAS

- Developing appropriate language.
Transformation
- How to enlarge and reduce shapes.
- Practical experience of rotating and reflecting shapes and objects.
Symmetry
- Practical experience of symmetrical patterns using various media (such as on pegboards) and through paper-folding.

Art and D&T activities, science, PE and music are all great contexts for introducing children to the vocabulary of transformations (enlargements, reflections, rotations and translations or slides) and symmetry, and allows them to investigate these ideas using paint, scissors and construction models. Young children spend some time in school each day in 'play' situations before 'tidy-up time'. Try to spend a little time looking for examples that can be used to stimulate and encourage children to use precise mathematical language.

Young children are fascinated by, not frightened of, complex vocabulary. This means that they will soon be trying out these words for themselves. You may hear them talking to one another about their 'symmetrical patterns with the bricks', for example. Many of the buildings, patterns and drawings that children make are symmetrical – they appear to enjoy the order and conformity.

BY THE END OF YR/P1 MOST CHILDREN SHOULD BE ABLE TO:

- make symmetrical shapes and patterns, for example, using 2-D and 3-D shapes and other materials including with folded paper and paint
- use a mirror to explore patterns
- use some words related to size and transformation, such as slide, around, above, turn.

BY THE END OF Y1/P2 MOST CHILDREN SHOULD BE ABLE TO:

- explore slide and turn in PE, art etc
- distinguish repeating patterns and symmetrical patterns;
- start talking about 'symmetry' in context, for example, in art activities
- make symmetrical patterns by cutting out or with paint.

BY THE END OF Y2/P3 MOST CHILDREN SHOULD BE ABLE TO:

- start to describe patterns made with translations (slides) *and* turns
- recognise and draw in one line of symmetry, vertically or horizontally, on a shape, or draw complex shapes and patterns with one line of symmetry, or complete a picture to be symmetrical.

SOME COMMON MISCONCEPTIONS

DIFFERENT DIRECTION, SAME SHAPE

Position in space is critical to transformation. The difficulties of orientation are similar to those for 2-D & 3-D Shapes (see Key Ideas on page 10). The idea that a shape is the same whatever its orientation is related to conservation.

Many young children are convinced that:

is different from:

This seems to be less of a problem with 3-D shapes – a cylinder is still a cylinder even if it falls over:

 or

This may be because the children are far more used to manipulating these shapes in all orientations in space – to build with or to roll in the case of the cylinder.

ENLARGING AND REDUCING SHAPES

When asked to enlarge a 2-D shape, the children are usually comfortable with extending one dimension (eg, rolling a Plasticine snake longer – see Length Key Ideas, page 74), but find the two difficult.

Try doubling a number of cubes. Separate the dimensions: first double the length of a line, then the height of a tower. Then enlarge a block of, say, four cubes.

Shadows are excellent for observing shapes that are larger or smaller. You may need to ask one child to lie on their shadow, draw round the shape with chalk and then draw round the shadow to prove how the shadow appears larger or smaller than the real person. Or use the OHP to show how an A4-sized drawing can be projected to cover a huge part of the wall. The children may be aware of how the font size on a computer can be changed so that their work can be printed larger or smaller than the original typed version.

ROTATING

Rotation about a point is easier to understand as it can be related to turning. The word 'rotate' could be introduced if you are looking at wheels or cogs or the hands on a clock face – and is attractively demonstrated in autumn with leaf prints:

The difficulties start when the children have to move (translate) the shape sideways and rotate it, rather than making a circle pattern.

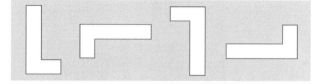

This is easier to start with using a physical shape with a reference point, for example, drawing around four red cubes and one blue cube:

It is important the children keep the shape flat and slide it before turning it. The problem here is that they associate 'turn' with 'turn it over' as in 'turn the page'. Point out that when they 'turn over in bed' they don't end up with their feet on the pillow! Encourage and be careful of your own precise language use.

SYMMETRY

Symmetry is not a repeat: there is sameness *and* reflection involved:

DDCD   DDDD

repeating pattern, but… symmetrical

Use and talk about mirror images, first in PE with partner work and then with pictures and plastic safety mirrors.

It is vital, when younger children are making symmetrical patterns and reflected patterns, that we use the correct vocabulary, so that their more formal use later is not completely alien to them. It is very easy to say, 'We are going to make a string pulling pattern this afternoon,' therefore failing to take the opportunity of using the word 'symmetry' and 'line of symmetry'. You may need to explain that you are making the other half so that the picture is complete.

Singing action songs such as 'Heads, shoulders, knees and toes' helps children to be aware of body symmetry. When discussing animals and plants, there are many opportunities to discuss symmetry. Leaves have a central midrib; the children can draw this and then one side of the leaf, fold and cut along the leaf edge. Alternatively, paper can be folded in half and a shape drawn and then cut out.

TRANSFORMATIONS & SYMMETRY

MAKE A BIGGER SQUARE

†† *Up to 10 children (in pairs)*
⏱ *About 20 minutes*

AIM
To investigate how to make larger squares using small squares.

WHAT YOU WILL NEED
Polydron, Clixi or a large number of 2-D squares (thin card or laminated paper), all of the same size; squared paper and pencils (optional).

WHAT TO DO
Hold up a square shape. Ask a child to look at, name and describe the shape you are holding. Ask the children to work in pairs to make a larger square, using more square shapes. When they have finished, ask:
● *Has everyone made a square? How do you know?*
● *How many small squares have you used?*
Now ask the children to make an even bigger square. When they have finished, ask:
● *How do you know that your square is bigger?*
● *How many small squares did you use to make your bigger square?*
You may want them to record their results by making smaller-scale drawings on squared paper.

DISCUSSION QUESTIONS
See above.

ASSESSMENT
Note whether the children can define a square as having four sides of the same length and four corners that are the same. Ask them to show you the sides of the larger (or even larger) square: note whether they are counting the outside edges of the big square, not the individual sides of the small squares.

EXTENSION
The children can try a similar activity with oblongs.

MAKE A SMALLER SQUARE

†† *About 10 children (in pairs)*
⏱ *About 20 minutes*

AIM
To investigate how to make a smaller square from a big square.

WHAT YOU WILL NEED
Squares of coloured paper, scissors, adhesive, blank paper.

WHAT TO DO
The children should work in pairs to facilitate co-operation and discussion. Give each pair a square of coloured paper. Ask them:
● *What shape is your paper?*
● *How do you know?*
● *Turn the paper so the corner is facing you. What shape is it now? [The children need to know that it is still a square.]*
Ask the children to fold their paper to make a smaller square, then show you the square. You may need to demonstrate, or ask a pair to do so. (See figure.) They need to fold the square in half each time. Check that they are making smaller squares, not triangles or oblongs.
● *How many folds did you make?*
● *When you folded the first time, what shape did you make?*
Ask each child to cut out one smaller square and stick it down on paper. Each pair will now have a small square each. Ask them to make an even smaller square with it, then stick this down on the paper.

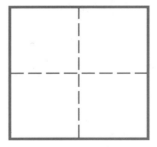

DISCUSSION QUESTIONS
● *How many times do you need to fold a big square to make a smaller square?*
● *How many smaller squares are there?*

● *Do you think there will always be four smaller squares?*

ASSESSMENT
Do the children understand that the smaller shape they make must be a square?

EXTENSION
● Pairs of children can experiment with large newspaper squares.
● They can try to make smaller oblongs and triangles.

MAKE A BIGGER CUBE

†† *About 10 children (in pairs)*
🕐 *About 20 minutes*

AIM
To investigate how to make bigger replicas of 3-D shapes.

WHAT YOU WILL NEED
Lots of interlocking cubes.

WHAT TO DO
Give each pair a cube and ask them to name and describe this 3-D shape. Now ask them to make a bigger cube. Check that they have all made a cube. Some pairs may have made a (non-cubic) cuboid using four small cubes. You may need to discuss the properties of a cube: it has six square faces, and twelve edges of the same length. Demonstrate how to count the faces and edges of the larger cube if necessary.

   If appropriate, ask the children to make a still larger cube.

DISCUSSION QUESTIONS
● *How many faces does a cube have?*
● *What shapes are the faces?*
● *Can you show me the faces on your larger cube?* [Check that the children are not pointing to the individual cubes.]
● *How many small cubes make a bigger cube?* [8 or 27.]
● *Can you show me how to count the edges on your larger cube?* [Check that they are not counting the sides of the individual squares.]

ASSESSMENT
Can the children describe and/or explain the properties of a cube?

EXTENSION
The children can try a similar activity using Polydron, linking to work on the relationships between 2-D and 3-D shapes (see page 18).

ROTATING LETTER SHAPES

†† *Whole class*
🕐 *About 15 minutes*

AIM
To investigate how shapes can be rotated.

WHAT YOU WILL NEED
A selection of plastic upper case letters or letter templates; a piece of paper with a large + sign on it for each child.

WHAT TO DO
Ask the children to choose a plastic letter (they may want to choose the first letter of their name), place it on the plus sign as shown below and draw round it. Demonstrate this on the board. Now ask them to turn

TRANSFORMATIONS & SYMMETRY

or rotate the letter round to the right (clockwise) until it reaches the next line, then draw round it again. They should repeat the process until the letter has completed the rotation.

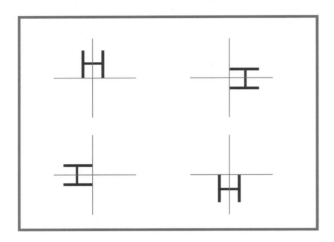

DISCUSSION QUESTIONS
● *How many times did you need to turn your letter for it to look the same as when you first drew it? [Two or four, depending on its shape.]*
● *Who can remember what we call this type of pattern? [You may want to discuss the word 'rotating' as 'going round like a wheel'.]*

ASSESSMENT
Check that the children are rotating the letter in the right direction, and sliding it rather than turning it over.

EXTENSIONS
● The children can rotate leaves by rubbing or printing with them.
● They can cut out several identical triangles from tissue paper and use them to create a rotating, overlapping pattern.
● They can cut out several identical shapes, use a split pin to hold them together and fan them out to make a rotating shape.
● They can use photocopiable page 43 to practise turning shapes by a quarter-turn.

SYMMETRICAL BUTTERFLIES

†† *About half the class*
🕐 *About 15 minutes*

AIM
To create symmetrical pictures.

WHAT YOU WILL NEED
Plain paper, paint and a brush for each child. (Shiny paper gives better results than absorbent paper.)

WHAT TO DO
Ask the children to fold a sheet of paper in half. Check that they are matching the corners before folding. Make a symmetrical butterfly or bird picture by painting and folding:
● For a butterfly, paint half the shape, fold quickly, unfold and allow to dry. Repeat for the wing pattern.
● For a bird, create an outline as above. Place blobs of paint within one wing outline. Coil a piece of string between the blobs, with both ends at the bottom of the card (see figure). Refold the card, hold both ends of the string together and pull sharply. Unfold to let the 'feathers' dry.

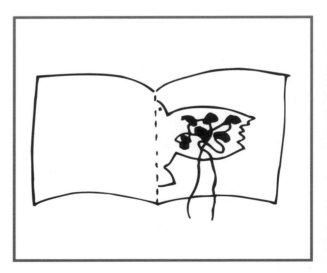

DISCUSSION QUESTIONS
● *What has happened to the opposite side of the paper?*
● *How has the picture on the blank side been made?*
● *How is the picture the same/different?*
● *Where do the two halves of the picture join? Why?*
Tell the children that the picture is **symmetrical**, and that the fold in the paper is the **line of symmetry**.

ASSESSMENT
Do the children remember the word 'symmetrical' and use it to describe the pattern of two reflecting images?

EXTENSIONS

● The children can fold a sheet of paper in quarters and cut patterns into the paper, then open it out and investigate the symmetrical pattern. Ask them: *How many lines of symmetry are there?* (Two.)

● They can use photocopiable page 42 to practise drawing symmetrical pictures.

MOVE IT

✝✝ *Whole class, then pairs*

🕐 *15 minutes demonstration, 20 minutes (per pair) computer time*

AIM

Exploring rotations

WHAT YOU WILL NEED

A computer drawing or painting program, photocopiable page 128. Some programs allow you to specify the amount of turn, but for this activity a simple 'Rotate 90°/180°' is sufficient.

WHAT TO DO

Demonstrate the rotation tools (or 'turn tools') of your computer graphics program to the class by turning a shape, a piece of clipart or a line of text. Alternatively, show one pair of children and then let them tutor another pair. It is useful to copy the original shape before transforming it, so that children can compare it 'before' and 'after'.

Ask the children to select a small piece of clipart or make a pattern from the basic shapes available. Show them how to copy and rotate their shape, then repeat this twice more so that they have the same image in four orientations. Interesting effects can be created in this way (see illustration). The children

can use the text tools to give their picture a title. They can use the writing frame on page 128 to describe how the picture was created.

DISCUSSION QUESTIONS

● *What will happen to that shape when it is rotated?*
● *How have you changed the shape?*
● *How did you create that pattern?*
● *Can you give someone else instructions to make the same pattern?*

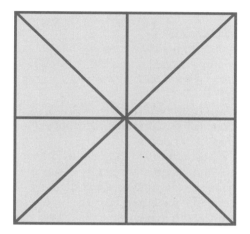

ASSESSMENT

Can the children predict the outcomes of various rotations? Can they describe what has happened to their shapes? Can they explain to a friend how to rotate shapes on screen?

EXTENSION

Introduce the other transformation tools in a similar way. Reflections (sometimes referred to as 'flips'), stretching, skewing and enlarging can all be used to produce interesting designs. The emphasis should be on fun exploration rather than on specific mathematical categorization of the transformations.

TRANSFORMATIONS & SYMMETRY

TRANSFORMATIONS & SYMMETRY

DOTTY DOGS

†† *Groups of 10 children, working individually*
🕑 *About 15 minutes*

AIM
To investigate a method of enlarging a shape.

WHAT YOU WILL NEED
Photocopiable page 37.

WHAT TO DO
Give each child a copy of page 37. Ask:
● *How many squares long is the dotty dog's tail?*
● *How long will the tail be if the dog's size is doubled?*
● *How long is his back?*
● *How long will his back be if you double the length?*
● *How high is his back?*
When the children have established how to double the size of the image, they can try drawing a dog twice as big for themselves. Check that they understand that **each part** of the dog needs to be double the length and width. If they seem confused, you may need to demonstrate with an enlarged copy of page 37 on the flip chart, asking the children to help you draw a dog that is double the size.

DISCUSSION QUESTIONS
● *What is double the body width?*
● *Can you tell me what double the body length will be?*

ASSESSMENT
Note whether the children understand the concept of doubling. For example, do they know that double 2 is 4 and so on? They need to be familiar with this concept in terms of number before they can apply it to shapes.

EXTENSIONS
● The children can make a shape on one pinboard with a rubber band, then enlarge the shape on another pinboard.
● They can draw their own pictures on dotted paper, then draw enlarged versions.
● Draw a grid over a simple picture and photocopy it, then ask the children to draw the same picture on a sheet with larger squares.

WHAT'S IN THE MIRROR?

†† *About 10 children*
🕑 *About 15 minutes*

AIM
To observe and predict how shapes are reflected.

WHAT YOU WILL NEED
Photocopiable page 38, a plastic mirror for each child.

WHAT TO DO
Give out copies of page 38. Ask the children to point to the flower, and to place their mirror on the horizontal line below the flower. Check that they are all holding the mirror in the correct position. Discuss (see below). Ask the children to draw the flower as they see it reflected in the mirror. They should be able to complete the sheet independently.

DISCUSSION QUESTIONS
● *How does the flower look in the mirror? [upside down] Why is that?*
● *What do you think the flower will look like if you place the mirror above the flower head? [upside*

down again] Try it – were you right?
- *What has happened to the '3'?*
- *How many windows are there now?*
- *Are the houses touching? Are the trees touching? Why/why not?*
- *How could you make the trees touch?*

ASSESSMENT

Can the children predict how many trees they will see before using the mirror? Can they explain why there are twice as many in the completed drawing?

EXTENSION

● The children can look into puddles or a water tray and describe what they see.
● If appropriate, the children could use a mirror to test which letters (photocopiable page 39) have **line symmetry**: if you put a mirror across them (either vertically or horizontally), will you still see the whole letter? Can they predict before testing?

PE REFLECTIONS

✝✝ *The whole class, working in pairs*
🕐 *About 20 minutes*

AIM

To make sequences of reflecting body shapes.

WHAT YOU WILL NEED

A large space (such as the school hall), a tamba or drum.

WHAT TO DO

Ask the children to listen as you make a short sequence with the tamba: three short beats, a rotating sound and then three short beats. Ask them to describe this sequence of sounds, and then to try moving to the sounds. Encourage them to experiment with different types of movement; you may want some children to demonstrate more adventurous patterns.

Once they are confident, ask the children to sit in pairs facing one another and imagine that they are looking at a mirror. They need to start in a reflecting shape, move apart on the three beats, turn around, move back together on the final three beats, and end by touching in a different reflecting shape. Check that all the children understand the task. It is often helpful to pair a more mature child with a younger child.

They will need to discuss their ideas in pairs (for two or three minutes) before they try making their reflecting pattern with the tamba. Go through the sequence two or three times to check that the children have memorized their movements. They may need time to discuss some changes and make a final check before they perform to the class. Sit the children in a large circle to watch pairs performing. You may want to limit this to four or five different pairs each week.

DISCUSSION QUESTIONS

- *Have Hannah and Jake made a reflecting pattern?*
- *How do you know?*
- *Which starting shape did you like best? Why?*
- *How did you know it was a reflecting shape?*

TRANSFORMATIONS & SYMMETRY

ASSESSMENT

Do the children start and finish with reflecting shapes? Can they explain why these are reflecting shapes?

EXTENSION

The children can try to create reflecting patterns for more complex tamba rhythms.

PEGBOARD SYMMETRY

†† About eight children
🕐 About ten minutes

AIM

To complete a symmetrical 2-D pattern.

WHAT YOU WILL NEED

A pegboard and pegs (in various colours) for each child; plastic mirrors as needed.

WHAT TO DO

Ask the children to tell you where 'halfway' will be on a pegboard. Draw a chalk line. Show them a simple array of pegs and ask them to help you complete the pattern. Use a mirror to check for symmetry.

The children work in pairs. Each child makes a multicoloured array of pegs on half of a pegboard. The pairs then swap boards, so that the other child can make the other half of a symmetrical pattern. Check that the children understand the vocabulary you have used.

Less able children could be limited to using fifteen pegs, in only two colours, to make the first half of the pattern. Allow them to use a mirror to complete the pattern if necessary.

DISCUSSION QUESTIONS

● *How can you check whether your pattern is symmetrical?*

ASSESSMENT

Ask the children to swap their completed pegboards and show you the line of symmetry on their partner's pegboard with a mirror.

EXTENSIONS

● The children can use Multilink boards to create symmetrical patterns.
● They can use photocopiable page 40 to draw half of a symmetrical pattern for their partner to complete.
● They can use photocopiable page 41 to practise drawing a symmetrical pattern without using a pegboard.

INTERLOCKING CUBES

†† Up to ten children, working in pairs
🕐 About 15 minutes

AIM

To complete a symmetrical 3-D shape.

WHAT YOU WILL NEED

Five interlocking cubes for each child, squared paper, photocopiable page 128.

WHAT TO DO

Ask each child to stick five cubes together to make a flat shape, then swap the shape with their partner. They should then complete a symmetrical shape with five more cubes. They will need to discuss where to start making the symmetrical pattern with their partner. When they are confident that they have completed the pattern, they can record it on squared paper and use the writing frame (page 128) to record how they solved the problem.

DISCUSSION QUESTIONS

● *Which shapes were hard/easy to make symmetrical?*
● *Why?*
● *How many colours did you need to complete the pattern?*

ASSESSMENT

Do the children complete the pattern symmetrically?

EXTENSION

Ask the children to give their partners instructions for making the shape symmetrical. This is very difficult unless the shape is flat!

NAME _____ DATE _____

DOTTY DOG

■ Use the dots to help you draw a dotty dog that is **twice as big** underneath the first one.

 How long is the new dog's tail? How tall is the new dog? Tell a teacher.

SEE 'DOTTY DOGS', PAGE 34.

MIRROR REFLECTIONS

■ Place your mirror along the thick line, then draw the reflection in the blank space.

 Check with your mirror to see what has happened.

 What has happened to the number 3? How many trees can you see? Tell a friend.

SEE 'WHAT'S IN THE MIRROR?', PAGE 34.

DEVELOPING SHAPE,
SPACE & MEASURES

TRANSFORMATIONS & SYMMETRY

NAME

DATE

LETTER SYMMETRY

■ Use a mirror to find the lines of symmetry in these letters.

Letter	No line of symmetry	Vertical line of symmetry	Horizontal line of symmetry
A			
B			
C			
D			
E			
F			
G			
H			
I			
J			
K			
L			
M			
N			
O			
P			
Q			
R			
S			
T			
U			
V			
W			
X			
Y			
Z			

 How many letters have no symmetry? Tell a teacher.

SEE 'WHAT'S IN THE MIRROR?', PAGE 34.

DEVELOPING SHAPE, SPACE & MEASURES

TRANSFORMATIONS & SYMMETRY

PEGBOARD SYMMETRY

■ Add pegs to the other side to make a symmetrical pattern.

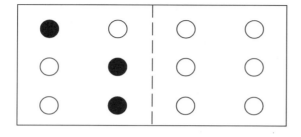

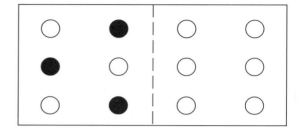

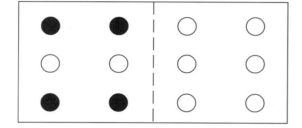

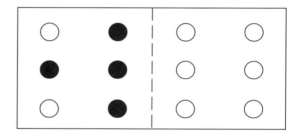

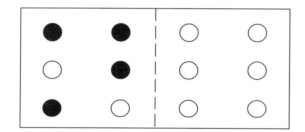

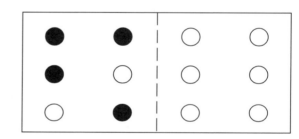

■ Draw some coloured pegs on the left-hand side of each pegboard. Now ask your partner to draw pegs on the right-hand side to make a symmetrical pattern.

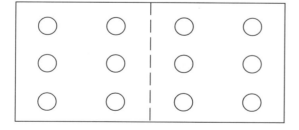

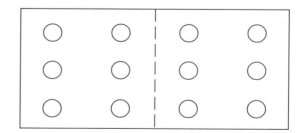

 Use a mirror to check that each pattern is symmetrical.

SEE 'PEGBOARD SYMMETRY', PAGE 36.

TRANSFORMATIONS & SYMMETRY

NAME   DATE

FLAG PATTERNS

■ Complete these flags to show symmetrical patterns.

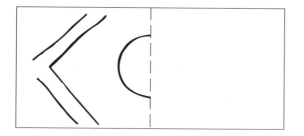
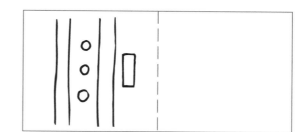

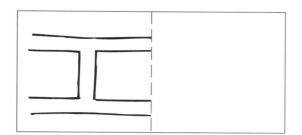
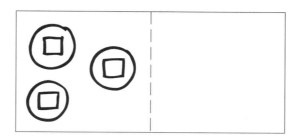

■ Draw your own design in the left-hand half of each flag.
Now your partner has to complete a symmetrical pattern.

■ Colour your flags, keeping the patterns symmetrical.

 Check each completed flag with a mirror.

SEE 'PEGBOARD SYMMETRY' PAGE 36.

TRANSFORMATIONS & SYMMETRY

SYMMETRICAL SHAPES

■ Cut out each oblong and fold it along the dotted line.

■ Cut out the shapes and stick them onto blank paper.

■ Complete each picture symmetrically.

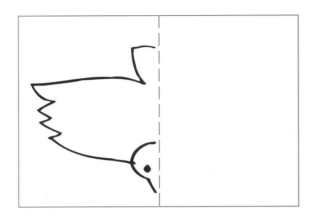

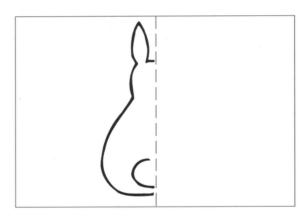
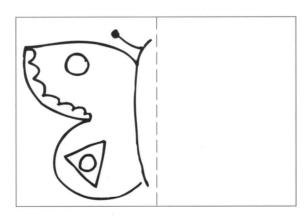
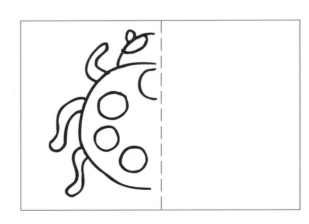

 How many dots does the complete ladybird have?
Tell a friend.

SEE 'SYMMETRICAL BUTTERFLIES', PAGE 32.

TRANSFORMATIONS & SYMMETRY

NAME   DATE

ROTATING SYMMETRY

■ Keep turning the shape and drawing what comes next.

  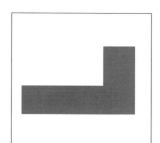 

■ Turn the flower by a quarter-turn and draw it in the box.

 How many quarter-turns before the sunflower is back to its original position? Tell the teacher.

SEE 'ROTATING LETTER SHAPES', PAGE 31.

**DEVELOPING SHAPE,
SPACE & MEASURES**

KEY IDEAS

- Developing general spatial awareness and the associated language of location.
- Being able to follow simple directions using the language of position and movement.
- Right angle/quarter turns in the context of giving directions.
- Compass points N, S, E and W.
- Simple co-ordinate grids.
- Pre-LOGO work.

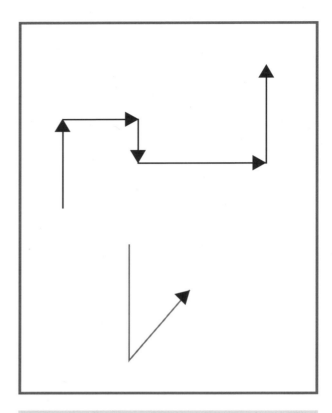

Throughout every day, you will have lots of opportunities to develop the children's awareness of their own position in space. When they are lining up, discuss their positions in the line: 'Put your hands up if you are standing behind/in front of Felix. Put your hand up if you are standing between Annie and Andrew.' Tidying-up, for example, provides numerous opportunities to extend this vocabulary: 'Can you put the books on the second shelf?'

At this young age, direction is largely about learning to give logically ordered instructions. When reading stories, discuss what happened at the beginning, what came next, what was the incident before or after…, and what happened at the end. This helps children become familiar with the pattern of the story. Many traditional stories lend themselves perfectly to sequencing. Consider 'The Three Little Pigs', 'The Gingerbread Man', 'The Enormous Turnip', 'The Little Red Hen and the Grains of Wheat' or 'Chicken Licken'.

Rosie's Walk by Pat Hutchins (Bodley Head) and *The Bears in the Night* by Stan and Jan Berenstain (Collins) use good positional vocabulary to describe journeys. These books can be memorised and used to act out the sequences. *The Bears in the Night* is ideal to inspire model-making. Then use plastic counting bears to make the journey up to Spook Hill and the return to the bedroom in the tree. Ask the children to make models using bricks, train tracks, play people and vehicles that will use the positional words in these books.

Observe the sequence of the day. What do we do at the beginning of the day, first thing in the morning? Do we go out to play before or after music? What will we be doing after lunch? And in PE, make sequences of movement on the floor. Using the beats of a tamba or moving across apparatus encourages children to become familiar with first, second, third, ...last, next to.

'Turns' are an essential part of giving directions. But that is really about experiencing (mostly right) angles. In this section of this book, we shall be thinking about 'turn' in contexts such as: 'Forward 3, turn right, forward 4, turn left…', rather than turning on a point as a precursor to angle work (see the 'Experiencing turn' section, starting on page 60).

BY THE END OF YR/P1 MOST CHILDREN SHOULD BE ABLE TO:

- follow and give simple instructions to move themselves or toys around a track or maze, developing the language of moving and sequencing instructions
- describe simply where other children, then objects, are located
- follow simple instructions to place play people or toys, for example, to put the car in the garage.

BY THE END OF Y1/P2 MOST CHILDREN SHOULD BE ABLE TO:

- use an increasing range of positional vocabulary, for example, opposite, direction, under, through
- describe an arrangement of objects or a single location
- give or follow instructions, including by programming a floor robot, to reach a particular position.

BY THE END OF Y2/P3 MOST CHILDREN SHOULD BE ABLE TO:

- use words such as route, quarter turn, or clockwise
- use clockwise/anticlockwise with understanding
- use 'grids' (eg, squared paper) to locate a position and give instructions to move within them
- devise instructions for a floor robot to navigate a plan
- recognise the compass points.

SOME COMMON MISCONCEPTIONS

MOVING IT, NOT ME

Since young children are used to identifying their position relative to the wider environment, they often find it difficult to transfer this skill to objects that don't have such contexts and so tend to move themselves *and* the object. For example:…

The next tricky step is moving from *Put the red car between the yellow cars* to the more abstract *Where is the red car?* The key is familiarity with the necessary language, built up in PE etc.

'BETWEEN-NESS'

If you ask, *What is between the square and the triangle?*, the answer should be 'The circle and the oblong', but many children will want to include the shapes in front and behind to make the 'between' location more precise. This is made more confusing still if there is more than one thing 'between' and you ask, for example, *How many children come between Robert and Mary?*

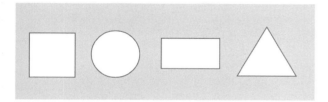

Start with one thing between. Help the children to see that, for example, the door is between the frames – it doesn't include the frame – or ask them to 'walk between the table and the chair' etc.

SEQUENCE MATTERS

Direction is basically about the sequence of instructions. You need to demonstrate that the order matters. This is best practised in PE, then in asking the children to retell stories: the pigs had to build their houses before the wolf could blow them down! Later, the children can walk out and then programme routes in LOGO and look at how changing the sequence of instructions alters what happens.

GETTING THE WHOLE STORY

It is also important to stress precision in giving and following instructions. Regularly, children will just 'hear' and do the last thing you say. For example, Jamie might stride across the classroom in response to 'Take four steps forward'. I tell him he needs more memory for the whole instruction! Start with short instructions and insist on careful listening and a precise response.

'WHICH WAY'S NORTH?'

Strictly speaking ability with the compass points is a Y3/P4 requirement. However, young children need to realize that the compass points (NSWE) are particular 'places' in space in the real world and don't vary. They can begin to understand this much earlier. Initially, you can introduce this idea indirectly by referring to the orientation of your school: *The car park always seems cold – it faces north* etc. Or draw the compass points on the playground and use these to find and record wind direction.

Draw a large picture of the UK. (Use an OHP to throw an image on to a wall to trace off.) Place this in the correct aspect on the classroom floor and draw a compass in the corner of the map. Mark in your nearest town and record holiday visits. Ask the children in which direction they would need to travel to arrive at their holiday destination. Name the countries of the UK and decide in which direction you would need to travel to visit these countries. When you are reading suitable stories, relate where you live to other places in the world using a globe: 'Are we south of…?'

GRIDS

Relating the position on a grid to a physical position is very difficult. If you need to go 'Two steps right and three steps forward', which way do you go first: which way is right on paper? Turning right or left on the grid needs the paper (or your head) to be turned too. To help the children, always show instructions in PE with your back to them so that your right is their right.

The children need to learn the conventions for showing location on a grid as early as possible: along then up. When the children have painted self-portraits display these in a grid (looking out of the individual panes of a window!). Label the grid with axis and co-ordinate labels to ask questions: *Where is Gemma's portrait? Whose picture is in B4? Who can read the co-ordinates for Matt's picture?*

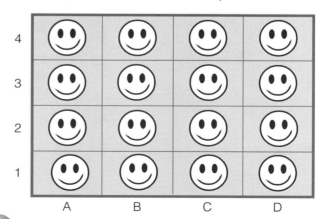

POSITION & DIRECTION

STANDING IN A ROW

†† *Whole class, sitting in a horseshoe shape*
⏱ *About 15 minutes*

AIM

To establish the vocabulary of position: first, second, third... last, behind, in front, between.

WHAT YOU WILL NEED

Five flashcards saying 'first', 'second' etc, with '1st', '2nd' etc on the reverse (see Extension).

WHAT TO DO

Ask about four children to stand in the central space, behind each other. Ask questions about position (see below). Most children will be able to answer these questions fairly easily; however, being able to describe the position that a child has been placed in ('second in line', 'between Raushan and Joe') is much more difficult. The children will need to experience using this vocabulary in many different situations.

DISCUSSION QUESTIONS

- *Who is standing in front of Molly?*
- *Who is the third person in the line?*
- *Who is last in the line?*
- *Who is standing between Molly and Joe?*

Rearrange the group by asking such questions as:

- *Who can put Molly between Nayaab and Raushan?*
- *Who can put Joe in front of Nayaab?*

Continue asking questions until the children are familiar with the vocabulary.

ASSESSMENT

Note whether the children can arrange themselves in a given order, and whether they can describe their position in terms of:

- First, second, third...
- In front of... behind... in between...

EXTENSIONS

- Give a group of five children flashcards with positional words ('first', 'second' etc). Ask them to arrange themselves in the correct order. Take away the cards, then redistribute them. Can they arrange themselves correctly?
- The children could complete photocopiable page 54 to practise using the language of position.
- They could complete photocopiable page 55 to practise using the language of order.

THE CALENDAR

†† *Whole class*
⏱ *A few minutes each day*

AIM

To become familiar with counting days as the 1st, 2nd, 3rd... of the month.

WHAT YOU WILL NEED

A calendar grid with the days of the week labelled down one side, the dates on separate squares that can be pinned onto the grid each day and a space to add the month at the top (see figure); drawing pins.

Monday					
Tuesday					
Wednesday					
Thursday					
Friday					
Saturday					
Sunday					

WHAT TO DO

Each day, ask a child to find the correct date and pin it into the correct space on the calendar chart. Ask questions about the date (see below).

Using a calendar gives the children valuable experience of recognizing time sequences: the days of the week, the dates (days of the month) and the months of the year. In addition, it helps them to become aware that although each week begins on a Monday, the day of the week on when a new month begins will vary.

DISCUSSION QUESTIONS

● *Who can read the date today? [for example, 'Monday the fifth of July 2001']*
● *Who can say what the date will be tomorrow?*
● *How do you know?*
● *What day of the week will it be tomorrow?*
● *How many more days are there until Sarah's birthday?*

ASSESSMENT

Note whether the children can read the date. The 1st, 2nd and 3rd of the month are more difficult than the others.

EXTENSIONS

● Ask children to write each day's date (in full) on the board. Use the calendar grid to help with the vocabulary. As the children mature, you may want to start recording the date in the form 5:7:2001. This will help the children to become familiar with ordering the months of the year.
● The children could complete photocopiable page 58 to connect the ordering of events in time with the ordering of objects in space.

SIMON SAYS

†† *Whole class, sitting in a circle*
🕐 *About ten minutes*

AIMS

To begin to distinguish between right and left. To follow instructions.

WHAT YOU WILL NEED

Self-adhesive labels marked 'right' or 'r' and 'left' or 'l' (if needed).

WHAT TO DO

Arrange the class in a semicircle around you. Play 'Simon Says', giving instructions such as *Put your right hand on your left shoulder.* If you need to demonstrate, it is essential that you stand at the front with your back to the class. You may prefer to play the game without eliminating children who make

mistakes (especially with Reception and Year 1 children).

It may be useful for the children to remember which hand they write with. Avoid confusion by explaining that most people write with their right hand, but some use their left hand. Children who are left-handed should remember, 'I write with my left hand' or 'I do not write with my right hand'. It often helps if they are grouped together.

Check that the children are listening and are able to follow the instructions. If the children are becoming confused, ask them to face the front of the class; then demonstrate by standing with your back to the children. You may want to ask some children to use self-adhesive labels on the backs of their hands (see above) to help them remember.

DISCUSSION QUESTIONS

● *Why is it easier for me to show you the moves if we're all facing the same way?*

ASSESSMENT

When the children are involved in this activity, it is easy to assess their competence in following the instructions.

EXTENSION

Make the instructions much more complicated, for example: *Put your right hand on your left knee.* Ask the children to take turns at being the teacher and giving instructions.

THE HOKEY COKEY

†† *Whole class, standing in a circle*
🕐 *About ten minutes*

AIMS

To practise knowledge of right and left. To follow instructions.

WHAT YOU WILL NEED

A large space – also confidence in singing!

WHAT TO DO

This activity should follow on from 'Simon says'. Arrange the children in a circle. Sing the 'Hokey Cokey' song together, with appropriate movements. Repeat this as an elimination game: children who make the wrong move (or no move) have to drop out. Speed up in the later stages.

You may need to check that the children can discriminate between the right and left sides of their body. If they are confused, play 'Simon says' again in spare moments.

DEVELOPING SHAPE,
SPACE & MEASURES

POSITION & DIRECTION

DISCUSSION QUESTIONS
● *If you all took a step to the right, what would happen?*
● *If you and the person oppposite you both raise your left hand, what do you notice?*

ASSESSMENT
Note whether the children are able to listen and to follow instructions correctly. Can they remember the sequence of actions?

EXTENSION
A group of children could play the commercial game 'Twister'.

KEEP TURNING RIGHT

†† *Whole class in the hall*
🕐 *About 5 minutes (at the start or end of a PE lesson)*

AIM
To establish how to make a right turn.

WHAT YOU WILL NEED
The hall, so the children can stand in their own space.

WHAT TO DO
Ask all the children to face the window. Turn your back to the children, then raise your right arm to point forwards. Ask the children to do the same. Indicate a right-hand quarter-turn with your arm and ask: *What will I be facing if I make a quarter-turn to the right?* (For example, the wall bars.)
   Ask the children to jump this quarter-turn to the right. Move with them, then repeat the process. Ask:

Where will we be facing if we make a quarter-turn to the right? (For example, the clock.) Continue making right-hand quarter-turns until you have completed a full turn (and are facing the window again).

DISCUSSION QUESTIONS
● *How many right-hand turns did we make to face the clock?*
● *How many more quarter-turns before we get back to facing the window?*
● *How many turns did we need to come all the way round?*

ASSESSMENT
Check (by glancing behind you) that all the children are raising their right hand and turning to the right each time. Note whether the children can predict where you will be facing after making each turn.

EXTENSIONS
● Ask the children to make half, three-quarter and whole turns to the right.
● The children could use photocopiable page 59 to consolidate their understanding of the terms 'forward', 'left' and 'right'.

WALKING A SQUARE

†† *Whole class*
🕐 *About 10 minutes*

AIM
To use directional vocabulary, including 'right' and 'left'.

WHAT YOU WILL NEED
The hall at the start or end of a PE lesson.

WHAT TO DO
This activity should follow on from 'Keep turning right'. Ask all the children to face the window. Tell them that you are going to give them directions for 'walking a square'. Remind them which is their right hand, and explain that each corner will be a quarter turn to the right. Now give instructions: *Take one step forward. Take a quarter-turn to the right. Take one step forward. Take a quarter-turn to the right...* Continue until they have walked the square.
   Check that the children are only making a quarter-turn each time. You may want to hold up a square shape to demonstrate this point.

DISCUSSION QUESTIONS
● *How many sides did we walk?*
● *What length were the sides of our squares?*

● *Do you think everyone had a side of the same length?*
● *Why/why not?*

ASSESSMENT

Can the children carry out the instructions for walking a square, making the correct turn for each corner?

EXTENSIONS

● The children can discuss how to walk a bigger square, then try it out.
● They can discuss how to walk an oblong shape, then try it out.
● Pairs can take turns to give each other instructions for walking a square or an oblong, then demonstrate to the class.

WHAT'S IN THE WINDOW?

†† *Up to 10 children*
🕐 *5 minutes explanation, 10 minutes independent activity*

AIM

To begin to read co-ordinates.

WHAT YOU WILL NEED

An enlarged version of photocopiable page 56; an A4 copy for each child.

WHAT TO DO

Pin up the enlarged copy of page 56 and ask the children: *Why do you think we have letters and numbers on the sides of the window?* Explain that it is a quick way of finding the position of something. Emphasize the rule that you must always read (or write) the letter or number on the bottom first, then the letter or number at the side. Use the analogy of going along the hallway and then up the stairs in a house.
   Ask the children:
● *Who can point to the Manx cat (the cat without a tail)?*
● *Can anyone tell me which square the Manx cat is sitting in?*
● *Who can point to the empty squares?*
● *Who can tell me the co-ordinates for those squares?*
Once you feel the children are confident, let them complete the sheet independently.

DISCUSSION QUESTIONS

When the group have completed the task, go through each question on the sheet and ask

individual children to explain their answers.

ASSESSMENT

This discussion method will give you the opportunity to check that all the children are happy with the task.

EXTENSIONS

● Give the children a blank co-ordinate grid and ask them to draw different objects in particular squares.
● The children can complete the map-reading activity on photocopiable page 57.

WHERE IS THE SUN?

†† *Whole class or group of about 10*
🕐 *10 minutes for first visit, 5 minutes for each later visit*

AIM

To know the four points of the compass.

WHAT YOU WILL NEED

The playground, chalk (or marker pens and wallpaper), a sunny day.

WHAT TO DO

This activity is easier in the winter months; try to choose a day when the forecast is for sun. Take the children into the playground first thing in the morning. Tell them that they must never look directly at the Sun, because it is very dangerous. However,

we can tell the Sun's position in the sky by looking at shadows.

Ask a child to draw around another child's shadow with chalk. Label the feet 'East' and the head 'West'. At 12 o'clock, ask another child to draw round the same child's shadow. Label the feet 'North' and the head 'South'. At three o'clock, the shadow will be in the opposite direction to the morning shadow: label the feet 'West' and the head 'East'. You may prefer to use large sheets of paper, such as the back of wallpaper, and marker pens. (Shadows in the early morning and late afternoon are very long in the winter.)

Encourage the children to compare the shadow lengths (for example, by measuring with their feet).

DISCUSSION QUESTIONS
● *What does the shadow tell you about where the Sun is?*
● *When you face your shadow, on what part of your body is the Sun shining?*
● *If the sun is in the east, which direction do you think Ellie's shadow will point in?*

ASSESSMENT
Note whether the children remember the four compass points. To check this, you might mark the compass points on the playground, then ask the children:
● *Which way is the wind blowing?*
● *What can you see to the east? To the south? [and so on]*

EXTENSION
● The children can use shadows to find out which parts of the school face each compass point. Again,

this is easier on sunny days in the winter, when the Sun is lower in the sky. Our hall windows face east, so it is sunny in the morning. The children walk west to the bus in the evening, so they are facing the sun.
● They can use the compass points to find the direction of the wind, then record it on a weather chart.

COMPASS POINTS

👥 *About 10 children*
🕐 *About 10–15 minutes*

AIM
To know the four points of the compass.

WHAT YOU WILL NEED
The playground, a compass, a large piece of paper, four stones, a marker pen, a metre ruler.

WHAT TO DO
Wedge down a large sheet of paper with four stones on the playground. Show the children a compass and ask them:
● *Do you know what this compass is for?*
● *What is written on it? [Pass it round for the children to look at in pairs.]*
● *Can anyone put it on the paper and turn it until the compass point is facing north?*

- *Can anyone lay the ruler on the paper in the same direction as the compass point?*
- *The ruler is now pointing north and south. Can anyone draw the north-south line and label it?*
- *Who can tell me the other directions on the compass? [East and west.]*
- *Who can put the ruler across the line so that it points east and west?*
- *Can anyone draw the east-west line and label it?*

DISCUSSION QUESTIONS

- *How did we know which direction was north?*
- *Could we find north without the compass now? [Yes, by referring to the compass points on the playground.]*

ASSESSMENT

Note whether the children can turn the compass to find north. Do they remember that south is opposite to north?

EXTENSION

- Ask the children to stand in a row facing north. Ask: *What can you see? Everyone turn to face east – what can you see now?* Continue until all four compass points have been observed.
- The children can fold a sheet of paper into four and label the compass points, then draw one significant feature from the playground at each compass point.
- They can use a length of wool and a compass to record the wind direction, then use a church or school weather vane to confirm.

THE RACE TRACK

†† Whole class, then small groups
⏱ 30 minutes

AIM

To explore position and direction using a floor robot.

WHAT YOU WILL NEED

A variety of obstacles (large bricks, crates, metre sticks), a programmable floor robot, an open floor space.

WHAT TO DO

Make up a course for a floor robot to negotiate, in the classroom or hall (some floor robots work best on non-carpeted areas). Initially, it is best to stick to right-angled turns. A suggested race track is shown below. The width of the circuit should be at least twice the width of the robot. Children should be able to walk the route comfortably.

Gather the class around the track. Place a child at the bottom right-hand corner, facing forwards. Now ask for instructions that will move the child around the circuit, such as ' two steps forward' and 'turn left'. Repeat this several times.

Now show the children the floor robot and remind them of the basic controls. Place the robot at the beginning of the circuit and explain that they will have to make the robot move around the circuit. If you have more than one robot, the circuit should be large enough to have two groups working simultaneously (they can start from a different point).

Encourage the children to start with small steps, such as moving the whole of the first length, then stopping and turning, then moving some more. With more practice, they should be able to build up a string of commands that will cause the robot to negotiate the whole circuit without stopping.

DISCUSSION QUESTIONS

- *How many steps forward should Jenny go?*
- *What direction should she turn now?*
- *What will happen if you tell the robot to move forward 3/turn left?*

ASSESSMENT

Are the children able to describe a route around the circuit accurately in words? Can they program a floor robot to move around the circuit?

EXTENSIONS

- The children can try sending the robot around the circuit in the other direction. What stays the same? What changes?
- They can design alternative circuits to try out.

POSITION & DIRECTION

GINGERBREAD MAN

†† *Whole class, then groups*
🕐 *About 20 minutes to revise the story sequence*

AIM
To establish the correct vocabulary for sequencing a story: first, second, third, at the beginning, after that, before that, last of all, at the end.

WHAT YOU WILL NEED
The story of 'The Gingerbread Man' (other stories could be used, such as 'The Enormous Turnip', 'The Little Red Hen and the Grains of Wheat' or 'Chicken Licken').

WHAT TO DO
Read the story, asking questions to establish that the children are familiar with the sequence of characters. Now ask the children to work in groups on retelling the story as a play. They should include a narration which uses sequence words (see 'Aim' above). They could make character masks in an art lesson. The groups should rehearse their play and then perform it to the rest of the class. Before they perform, remind them that the audience will be checking that the characters appear in the correct order.

DISCUSSION QUESTIONS
Ask the group performing to ask the audience one question, such as: *Which animal came after the Old Man? Who was the third character? How many characters came before the Little Dog? Who was the first person to try and catch the Little Gingerbread Man?* You may want to prepare these in advance.

ASSESSMENT
Do the children know the sequence of characters following the gingerbread man? Do they understand and use the vocabulary of sequencing?

EXTENSION
The children can make an interactive wall display showing the characters from the story. Pin on positional labels in the wrong places. Ask the children to point out and rectify the mistakes.

A MODEL VILLAGE

†† *About 8 children*
🕐 *About 20 minutes*

AIM
To use positional language (including 'under' and 'over') correctly.

WHAT YOU WILL NEED
A selection of modelling components: play people, animals, vehicles, bricks, railways and so on.

WHAT TO DO
Ask the children to design a model village using the

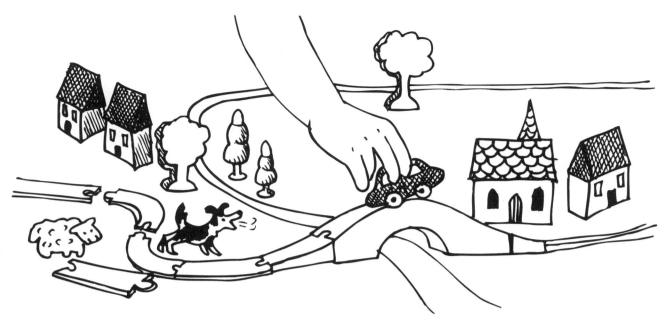

materials available. They should include a bridge with something going over it and something else going under it. When they have completed the model, you may want the whole class to be involved in a discussion of it.

DISCUSSION QUESTIONS
Ask the children who have made the model to say one thing each about their model; remind them to use positional language. Encourage other children to become involved by asking specific questions:
- *Can you push the red car under the bridge?*
- *Can you fly the aeroplane over the church?*
- *Can you take the dog through the sheep field?*

ASSESSMENT
Do the children make accurate statements using the correct vocabulary?

VARIATION
- The children can make a model from construction or junk materials to retell the story of *The Bears in the Night* by Stan and Jan Berenstain (Collins), then use Compare Bears to tell the story. The story of *Rosie's Walk* by Pat Hutchins (Bodley Head) is also ideal for positional language.

MAKE A SEQUENCE

†† *Whole class, working in groups*
🕐 *About 20 minutes*

AIMS
To develop a sequence of movements. To use the positional words 'over', 'under' and 'along'.

WHAT YOU WILL NEED
A PE bench, a mat and floor space for each group.

WHAT TO DO
Ask the children to design a sequence of movements that involves travelling **over**, **under** and **along** the two pieces of apparatus. You may want to limit the 'going under' to the bench! They can start in any place on the apparatus or floor, and the sequence can be in any order.

While the children are experimenting with their sequences, you may need to remind them to think of the three movements. When the groups are ready, they can perform their sequences to the class. The children observing need to be ready to answer questions (see below).

DISCUSSION QUESTIONS
- *Did Josh use the three movements?*
- *How did he go over the apparatus?*
- *Was Heather's sequence in the same order?*
- *How was the order different?*

ASSESSMENT
Do the children use the correct sequence of positional terms to answer questions about what they see?

EXTENSIONS
- Ask the children to perform each of the three movements, in a given order, on the mat or on the bench. Repeat, changing the order and the piece of apparatus.
- Add extra instructions to make the sequence longer – for example, 'Go between two objects and round a piece of apparatus.'
- Play 'Follow my leader', with the leader giving instructions for the sequence and the rest of the children carrying them out.

NAME **DATE**

THE PET SHOP

| above | below | between | next to |

■ Finish these sentences by writing position words from the list above.

The snake is _____ the rabbit.

The tortoise is _____ the cat.

The rabbit is _____ the tortoise.

The cat is _____ the snake and the dog.

The rabbit is _____ the snake.

 Which animal is between the rabbit and the mouse? Do you and your friend agree?

SEE 'STANDING IN A ROW', PAGE 46.

POSITION & DIRECTION

NAME   DATE

CATS ON CUSHIONS

first	second	third	fourth	fifth
1st	2nd	3rd	4th	5th

- Draw a black cat on the fourth cushion.
- Draw a spotted cat on the first cushion.
- Draw a ginger cat on the third cushion.
- Draw a white cat on the second cushion.
- Draw a tabby cat on the fifth cushion.

- Write in the missing position numbers below. The first one has been done for you.

The spotted cat is on the 1st cushion.

The ginger cat is on the _____ cushion.

The black cat is on the _____ cushion.

 Which cat is sitting on the fourth cushion? Tell a friend.

SEE 'STANDING IN A ROW', PAGE 46.

DEVELOPING SHAPE,
SPACE & MEASURES

POSITION & DIRECTION

50°

NAME _____   DATE _____

WHAT'S IN THE WINDOW?

A   B   C   D

■ Draw a kitten in window D2.
■ Draw a ginger cat in window D1.

 Write down the answers to these questions:

■ What is in window C3? _____

■ What is in window A3? _____

■ How many cats are in window C1? _____

SEE 'WHAT'S IN THE WINDOW?', PAGE 49.

POSITION & DIRECTION

NAME _____ **DATE** _____

A VILLAGE MAP

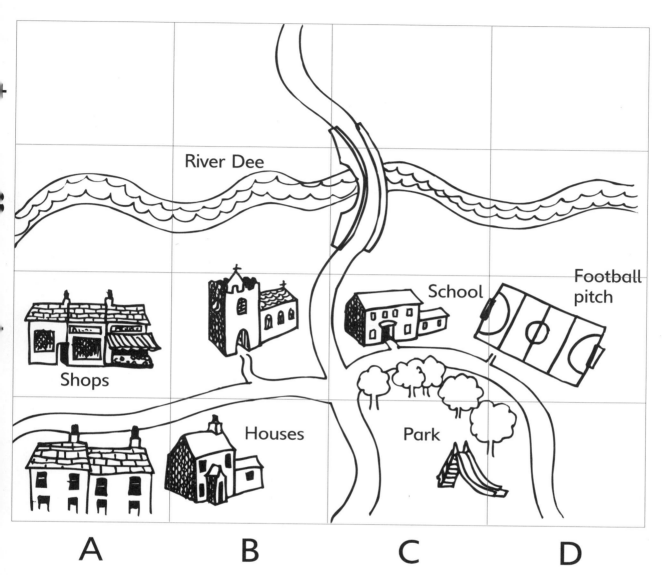

A   B   C   D

- The church is in which part of the map? _____
- Draw a swing in C1.
- Draw four sheep in C4.
- Does the bridge go over the river or under it? _____
- Use a red crayon to show your walk from the school to the field of sheep.

 Tell the teacher what part of the town the swing belongs to.

SEE 'WHAT'S IN THE WINDOW?', PAGE 49.

DEVELOPING SHAPE,
SPACE & MEASURES

POSITION & DIRECTION

NAME _____ **DATE** _____

THE SCHOOL 100M RACE

- _____ was first in the race.

- _____ was last in the race.

- _____ and _____ came between
Siân and Jon.

- Who came next after Siân? _____

- Who was in front of Megan? _____

 Tell a friend who came second in the race.

SEE 'THE CALENDAR', PAGE 46.

**DEVELOPING SHAPE,
SPACE & MEASURES**

NAME _____   DATE _____

FOLLOW THE PATH

■ Help Fido find his way along the path by writing instructions. Use the words in the list below to help you. Colour in each part of the path as Fido goes along.

right	left	forward	stop

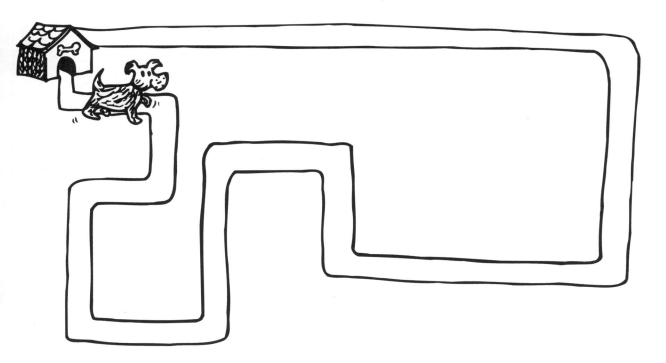

1. Forward, stop and turn right.

2. Forward, stop and turn _____ .

■ Carry on writing instructions on the back of this sheet.

 Tell a friend how many corners Fido needed to turn before he could get back to his kennel.

SEE 'KEEP TURNING RIGHT', PAGE 48.

DEVELOPING SHAPE,
SPACE & MEASURES

POSITION & DIRECTION

KEY IDEAS

- Whole turns, half turns and quarter turns.
- Quarter turns as 'right angles'.
- Angles/turns that are 'smaller than…' or 'greater than…'.

Young children soon become familiar with the words 'turn' and 'turning': *Can you turn to face the front? Can you turn the page over? Can you turn your socks the right way? They are inside out. Turn the key in the lock. The engine turned over.*

However, using the term mathematically will need to be explained because the turn will be a *measured* turn – an angle.

We tend not to use degrees for angles in Key Stage 1/Primary 1–3, but once the children are using the Roamer or other ICT packages they will need to become familiar with at least 90 (degrees) as being a ¼ turn. Initially, we measure using ¼, ½, ¾ and whole turns and later the term 'right angle'.

The children need to experience these maths concepts in PE and creative contexts; in less formal situations during their Reception and Year 1/Primary 1 and 2. They need to be able to visualize these movements in space for programming the floor robots etc.

They will use these fractions when working with an analogue clock: quarter past, quarter to and half past. It is worth noting that while they will also be developing familiarity with halving and quartering numbers, this is very different from ½ and ¼ turns and the skills are not easily transferable.

BY THE END OF YR/P1 MOST CHILDREN SHOULD BE ABLE TO:

- talk about and have experience of things that turn, for example, wheels, nuts and bolts, screw-top lids and so on.

BY THE END OF Y1/P2 MOST CHILDREN SHOULD BE ABLE TO:

- relate turn to the environment, eg keys, clocks, door hinges and so on
- use whole and half turns with understanding.

BY THE END OF Y2/P3 MOST CHILDREN SHOULD BE ABLE TO:

- extend to quarter turns and clockwise/anti-clockwise
- identify static right angles in the environment
- make quarter and half turns from the same and then different starting positions using apparatus such as Geostrips.

SOME COMMON MISCONCEPTIONS

LEFT ANGLES?

Most children will, hopefully, have experienced turning to the right and to the left before being asked to 'turn so many right angles'. A common misconception is that if we have right angles, we must have 'left' angles. I have experienced a child who would only measure right angles facing the right when investigating right angles as a shared maths homework. Give (or ask the class to call out) directions for walking routes (perhaps when blindfolded) that involve right and left turns. If you let the children try it blindfolded, make sure that there are no steps or dangerous obstacles in the way.

When practising turns in class or in PE, ask the children to stand and face one direction, for example the chalkboard (they'll need a reference point) and ask, for example: *Can you turn to face the door?* (This turn should be a ¼ turn to the right. You may need to discuss the quickest turn to arrive in this position.) *Can you turn again to face the display board? How many quarter turns have you taken? How many more turns before you are back where we started?* It is much easier in this instance to always refer to turning to the right.

MORE THAN A MEASURE

It is essential that children experience using right angles as a turn, otherwise they become fixed in the concept that an angle is not a turn but a static measure.

Many teachers introduce a right-angled corner as a 'square corner'. As the children mature, they need to use the correct vocabulary, so it is preferable to use the two expressions at the same time.

CLOCK WISE?

The clock 'starts' at 12, so which way is the start if we go 'clockwise'? You can avoid this problem by introducing 'clockwise' through circle time or in PE whenever you are 'going round the circle'. With wind-up toys, remind the children that these wind in a clockwise direction. Unscrewing the lid of a jar and turning a doorknob both involve turning in a clockwise direction.

When children are using card or plastic clocks for work on time remind them that the hands must turn in a clockwise direction, of course. And explain that we can't go back in time – against the clock – so that direction is anti-clockwise.

EXPERIENCING TURNS

TURNING RIGHT ANGLES

†† *Whole class*
🕒 *About 5 minutes*

AIM
To establish that a right angle is a quarter-turn.

WHAT YOU WILL NEED
Space for each child to stand and move easily.

WHAT TO DO
This could be done at the start or end of a PE lesson. The children should be familiar with making quarter-turns to the right. Repeat the activity 'Keep turning right' (see page 48) with the children, but using the language of angles and asking for left as well as right turns:
● *Where will I be facing if I turn one right angle to the right?*
● *If you turn one right angle to the right, where will you be facing? Show me.*
● *If you turn back one right angle to the left, where will you be facing? Show me.*
Note that many children become confused about the expression 'right angle', confusing it with 'right-hand turn' and 'left-hand turn'. It is essential for them to be aware that right angles can face in any direction. Point out that the phrase 'right angle' originally meant 'correct angle' in the context of building.

DISCUSSION QUESTIONS
See above. You could also ask children to show you a right angle with their arm or leg.

ASSESSMENT
Check that the children are making a quarter turn each time.

EXTENSIONS
● Ask the children to make two right-angled turns to the right and one right-angled turn to the left. Can they predict what they will be facing when they finish?
● Make a floor map with right angles. Ask the children to work in pairs, giving each other instructions for walking the pathway (for example, 'Forward one step, turn a right angle to the left, forward two steps'). Alternatively, photocopiable page 59 could be used.
● The children can program the Roamer to follow a pathway. It usually helps if they write their instructions down first.

ALL THE WAY ROUND

†† *Whole class*
🕒 *About 5 minutes*

AIM
To experience turn by an angle greater than a right angle.

WHAT YOU WILL NEED
Space for each child to stand and move easily.

WHAT TO DO
This could be done at the start or end of a PE lesson. Ask the children to face the window. Rehearse right-angled turns to the right and left, then ask:
● *If you turned halfway round, where would you end up facing?*
● *Can you all show me?*
● *How many right-angled turns have you made?*
● *If you turned all the way round, one whole turn, where would you be facing?*
● *How many right-angled turns will you have made?*

DISCUSSION QUESTIONS
● *Who can show me a right-angled turn?*
● *How far do you need to turn to make a right angle?*

ASSESSMENT
● Can all the children make a right-angled turn?
● Can they all make half and whole turns?

EXPERIENCING TURNS

Why/why not?
● *What will you need to do to make your picture upside down?*
● *How many right-angled turns do you need to make your picture the right way up again? Try it.*
● *How many times have you turned your picture altogether?*

ASSESSMENT
Note whether all the children can turn the pictures repeatedly by a right angle and explain the effect. Do they understand that four right-angled turns make a complete turn?

EXTENSION
Display sketches that the children have drawn (for example, of a tree or a house). Pin these up so that they can be rotated to show right-angled turns. You may want to add instructions such as: *Draw a picture to show how the tree will look if it is turned by two right angles. Check after drawing to see whether you were correct.*

EXTENSION
Ask the children to work in pairs, giving each other instructions for turning. They could follow a given pattern, or devise their own. Ask some pairs to demonstrate giving and following instructions.

TURNING A PICTURE

†† *About 10 children*
🕐 *About 20 minutes*

AIM
To know that four right-angled turns make a whole turn.

WHAT YOU WILL NEED
Individual pictures of the children (drawn or painted, perhaps as part of a topic on 'Ourselves').

WHAT TO DO
Ask the children to place their pictures face up on the table in front of them, then turn the picture one right angle to the right. Ask questions as shown below.

DISCUSSION QUESTIONS
● *What has happened to your picture?*
● *Why is your picture sideways?*
● *Is everyone's picture facing in the same direction?*

TURNING A SHAPE

†† *Up to 10 children*
🕐 *About 20 minutes*

AIM
To understand the effect of turning a 2-D shape by right angles.

WHAT YOU WILL NEED
Squared paper, coloured pencils and four interlocking cubes for each child, photocopiable page 128.

WHAT TO DO
Give the children exact instructions for making a shape:
● *Take four cubes – red, blue, green and yellow.*
● *Put the red and yellow cubes together. Lay them on the table horizontally, with the red on the left and the yellow on the right.*
● *Fix the blue cube under the red cube. It should be on the left.*
● *Where do you think we should fix the green cube to make a cuboid with a square face? That's right, fix it under the yellow cube.*
Check that each child has made the shape correctly. Ask the children to colour four squares on paper to match the colours on their shape.
  Now ask the children to turn their shape one right angle to the right. Check that they have done this correctly. You may want to ask:

EXPERIENCING TURNS

● *Which colour is in the top left-hand corner now?*
● *Why?*
Ask them to colour four squares on paper to show the new arrangement. Continue until they have drawn the pattern for each quarter-turn. Finally, they can use the writing frame (page 128) to record what they have found out.

You may need to pair less confident children with more confident children. This will be easier if they are sitting in rows, rather than around tables.

DISCUSSION QUESTIONS
See above.

ASSESSMENT
Check while asking questions that each child is following the instructions correctly. It is important that the children turn the shape by a quarter-turn each time and recognize that this can be called a right-angled turn.

EXTENSION
The children can make and record shapes using more colours.

MAKE A RIGHT ANGLE

✝✝ *Up to 10 children*
🕒 *About 20 minutes*

AIMS
To make a right angle. To investigate right angles in 2-D shapes.

WHAT YOU WILL NEED
Square pieces of paper, a selection of flat plastic or thin card 2-D shapes, photocopiable page 48. (You may want to make enlarged copies of the shapes from page 68 on card.)

WHAT TO DO
Ask the children to fold a square piece of paper into four diagonally to make a right angle (see figure). Tell them that they can use this as a right angle tester. Ask them to look at the first shape on page 68, find a plastic or card shape to match it, then test it for right angles. They should be able to continue independently with the sheet.

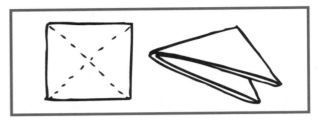

DISCUSSION QUESTIONS
Looking at the first shape together:
● *What is the first shape?*
● *How do you know?*
● *Can you find a shape to match this triangle?*
● *How many right angles do you think it has?*
● *Can you point to the corner that you think is a right angle?*
As the children are working through the sheet:
● *Which shape has the most right angles? How many right angles does it have?*
● *Could you have a 2-D shape with more than four right angles?*

ASSESSMENT
Check that the children identify and test the right angles correctly.

EXTENSION
The children can use pinboards and rubber bands to investigate whether there are any 2-D shapes with more than four right angles. They can record their findings [irregular shapes only] on dotted paper.

BODY RIGHT ANGLES

✝✝ *Whole class*
🕒 *About 10 minutes*

AIM
To make right-angled body shapes.

WHAT YOU WILL NEED
A tamba or drum, the school hall.

WHAT TO DO
In a PE lesson, ask the children to sit on the floor.

Ask them:
● *Can you bend your hand at the wrist to make a right angle?*
● *Can you make a matching right angle with your other hand?*
● *Now try using your elbows to make two right angles on each arm.*
Continue exploring right angles with the legs and body. Use the tamba to make short staccato beats, while the children make jerky right-angled shapes with their joints as they move around.

This is an ideal activity for a science topic on 'Ourselves': exploring how we move and how joints work.

DISCUSSION QUESTIONS
● *How many right angle bends has Hassan made? Can we count them out?*
● *Can anyone make more right angle bends?*

ASSESSMENT
● Ask the children to make three right-angled shapes with their legs as they move (hip, knee and ankle).
● Display some arm and leg angles: can they recognize which are right angles?

EXTENSIONS
● The children can work in pairs to make right-angled mirror images.
● They can make card models of dancers with split-pin paper fasteners at the joints, then move the limbs to make various right angles (see picture).

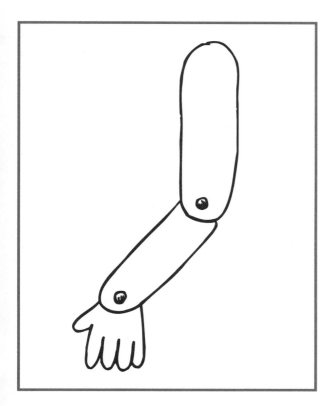

CLOCK RIGHT ANGLES

†† *About 8 children*
🕐 *About 20 minutes*

AIM
To investigate angles as a measure of turn.

WHAT YOU WILL NEED
A geared clock for demonstration, more geared clocks or card clocks (you may be able to borrow geared clocks from other classes), photocopiable page 70.

WHAT TO DO
Do not worry if the children cannot read the time on a clock: it is not necessary for this activity. Display a geared clock and ask the children to look carefully as you move the hands into the 3 o'clock position. Ask:
● *Can you all see the angle between the two hands?*
● *Can you remember what this type of angle is called?*
● *What will I need to do to make this angle greater than a right angle?*
● *What will I need to do to make this angle smaller than a right angle?*
Make sure the children understand that the angle is the amount of **turn** between the two hands. Display 4 o'clock on the clock face and ask: *Who can tell me what type of angle this could be?* ('More than a right angle.') Move the hands by five minutes and repeat the question. Carry on asking at each five-minute interval.

Give each pair of children a geared clock (or a card clock for each child), and ask questions as detailed below. If the children are confident with this, they should be able to work in pairs to complete page 70.

DISCUSSION QUESTIONS
● *Can you all show me a time when the hands are exactly a right angle?*
● *Can you all show me a time when the hands are at an angle greater than a right angle?*

ASSESSMENT
Note whether the children are certain of right angles. Can they make angles greater and smaller than right angles?

EXPERIENCING TURNS

EXPERIENCING TURNS

RIGHT ANGLES IN A CIRCLE

†† Up to 10 children
🕐 About 20 minutes

AIM
To investigate right angles in a circle.

WHAT YOU WILL NEED
Paper squares and circles, scissors.

WHAT TO DO
Ask the children to make a right angle measure using a paper square (see page 64). Now ask them to fold a paper circle in half and then into quarters, then cut along the folds to make four quarter-circles. Ask:
● What is the angle in each part of the circle called?
● How could you check this?
Ask the children to try this (see figure). Now ask them:
● How many right angles have you cut from the circle?
● Can you put the four right angles back together to make a circle?

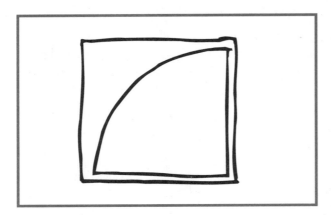

DISCUSSION QUESTIONS
● How many right angles are there in a circle?
● If a quarter circle is folded in half, will the angle be greater or smaller than a right angle?

ASSESSMENT
Note, by checking the children's work, whether they recognize that a circle can be divided into four right angles.

VARIATION
The children can quarter small circular cakes, salt dough circles, circle patterns or favourite meal collages and discuss how each of the four quartered wedges has a right angle.

RIGHT ANGLES IN LETTERS

†† About 10 children, working in pairs
🕐 About 20 minutes

AIM
To investigate right angles in upper-case letters.

WHAT YOU WILL NEED
A set of upper-case letters (plastic, wooden, magnetic or card), right angle measures (from 'Right angles in a circle'), photocopiable page 69.

WHAT TO DO
Give each child a copy of page 69 and a right angle measure. Revise measuring right angles by asking:
● What shape is the photocopied sheet? [oblong]
● What do we call the corners on an oblong? [right angles]
● How can you check that they are right angles?
Now ask the children to find out how many right angles each upper-case (capital) letter on the sheet has. When they have completed the sheet, they should discuss their findings with a partner and check any cases where they disagree.

DISCUSSION QUESTIONS
● Do all your results agree with your partner's results?
● Which letters were the most difficult to measure? Why?

● *Which letters were easy to agree about? Why?*

ASSESSMENT
Note whether the children identified right and non-right angles correctly. It may be useful to pin up a few large letters and ask children to check for right angles.

EXTENSION
The children can make 'calculator numbers' with strips of coloured card and stick them onto paper, then investigate the right angles in them.

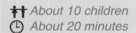

ANGLES IN 2-D SHAPES

†† About 10 children
🕐 About 20 minutes

AIM
To investigate angles that are greater or smaller than a right angle.

WHAT YOU WILL NEED
Salt dough pizzas or painted circular cakes, made by the children in an art or technology lesson; two geostrips (oblong card strips) and a split-pin paper fastener for each child; photocopiable page 71. Before the lesson, you will need to slice each of the salt dough circles into a set of different-sized wedges (the same for each circle).

WHAT TO DO
Ask the children to join two geostrips with a paper fastener to make an angle. Ask them:

● *Can you open the geostrip to show me an angle that is smaller than a right angle?*
● *How can you check? [With the corner of a sheet of paper.]*
● *Can you all show me an angle with your geostrips that is greater than a right angle?*
● *How can you check?*

The children should now measure the angles on their cake wedges and sort them into three groups: 'Greater than a right angle', 'Smaller than a right angle' and 'Exactly a right angle'. Pairs of children should compare their results and check for agreement. The pizza wedges could be displayed in sets, labelled as above. Ask the children to complete photocopiable page 71.

DISCUSSION QUESTIONS
When the children have completed the task, ask them:
● *Can you all show me a wedge that has an angle greater than a right angle? [You may want to pin up a right angle measure and ask some children to demonstrate their angles.]*
● *Does anyone have an angle that they think is a right angle?*
● *How can we check?*

ASSESSMENT
Are the children beginning to make accurate judgements before measuring the angles?

EXTENSIONS
● The children could look for angles in various 2-D shapes that are greater or smaller than a right angle.
● They could use pinboards and rubber bands to make 2-D shapes with angles greater or smaller than a right angle, perhaps recording them on dotted paper.

NAME _____   DATE _____

RIGHT ANGLES IN 2-D SHAPES

Shape	How many right angles?					
	0	1	2	3	4	5
triangle						
circle						
oblong						
pentagon						
octagon						
octagon						
hexagon						
hexagon						

 How many shapes have exactly **four** right angles?
Colour these shapes red. Does your friend agree?

SEE 'MAKE A RIGHT ANGLE', PAGE 64.

NAME   DATE

RIGHT ANGLES IN CAPITAL LETTERS

Letter	How many right angles?					
	0	1	2	3	4	5
A						
B						
C						
D						
E						
F						
G						
H						
I						
J						
K						
L						
M						
N						
O						
P						
Q						
R						
S						
T						
U						
V						
W						
X						
Y						
Z						

 Which letter has the most right angles? Write it down.

SEE 'RIGHT ANGLES IN LETTERS', PAGE 66.

**DEVELOPING SHAPE,
SPACE & MEASURES**

NAME

DATE

CLOCK RIGHT ANGLES

right angle	greater than a right angle	smaller than a right angle

■ Write under each clock what type of angle it shows.

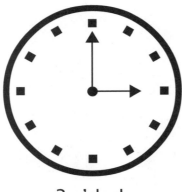

3 o'clock

5 o'clock

11 o'clock

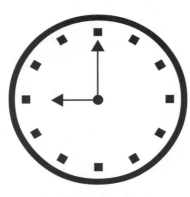

9 o'clock

1 o'clock

quarter past 6

 How many right angles does the clock show in an hour? Tell the teacher.

SEE 'CLOCK RIGHT ANGLES' PAGE 65.

DEVELOPING SHAPE,
SPACE & MEASURES

PIZZA SLICE ANGLES

■ Draw a line from each slice of pizza to the label which describes what type of angle the slice has.

right angle	greater than a right angle	smaller than a right angle

 How could you test whether the slices of pizza are right angles? Tell a friend.

SEE 'ANGLES IN 2-D SHAPES', PAGE 67.

EXPERIENCING TURNS

LENGTH

long

longer

longest

tall   *taller*   *tallest*

short   *shorter*   *shortest*

MASS

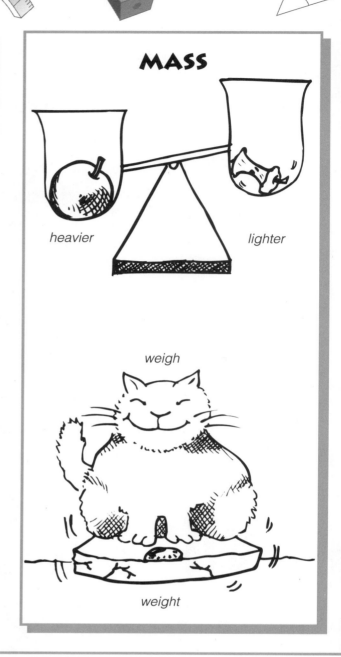

heavier   *lighter*

weigh

weight

TIME

days

Monday
Tuesday
Wednesday
Thursday
Friday
Saturday
Sunday

months and seasons

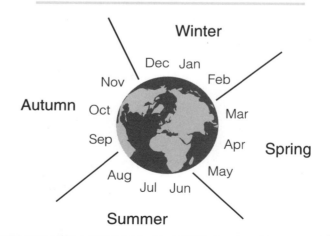

Winter

Dec Jan

Nov Feb

Autumn Oct   Mar

Sep   Apr   Spring

Aug   May

Jul Jun

Summer

CAPACITY

half full

empty

full

UNITS

100 centimetres = 1 metre

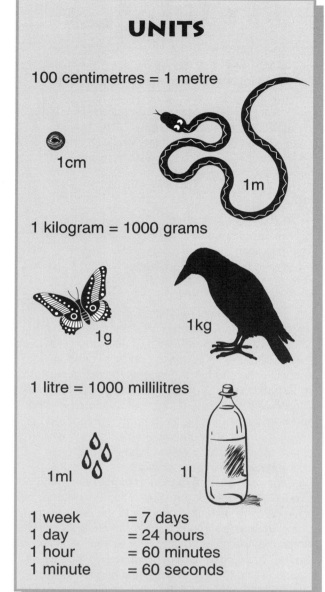

1cm

1m

1 kilogram = 1000 grams

1g

1kg

1 litre = 1000 millilitres

1ml

1l

1 week	= 7 days
1 day	= 24 hours
1 hour	= 60 minutes
1 minute	= 60 seconds

The minute hand is long and thin and rushes round the clock once in every hour.

4:05

The hour hand is short and fat and goes from one number to the next in every hour.

KEY IDEAS

- Being able to compare and order by length.
- Sorting objects by length, including by starting to compare them to a standard measure such as ½m.
- Estimating using non-standard units.
- Starting to use standard units of metre and centimetre, including ½m and ¼m.
- Practical experience that a length does not change with its orientation.
- Developing logic about the relationships between the sizes and order of objects.
- Starting to develop a practical 'feel' for area and perimeter of shapes. For example, perimeter as an extension of length (that is, 'the "length" all the way round') or area as 'covering'.

Length is the easiest measure for children to understand. Many children arrive at school able to select the longest pencil from three or four. However, they will be unable to use the correct vocabulary and will only refer to the biggest/smallest pencil. It is important that children are given opportunities when playing to discuss the things that they are building and constructing using the correct terminology. For example, *How do you know that William's tower is higher than Hassan's tower? Who can make the shortest tower using ten bricks?*

Length can also be extended to measuring the dimensions that bound a shape: the lengths that join up to give the distance round, and the area inside. Unfortunately, 'perimeter' and 'circumference' will be words that the children only hear at school! However, they will have often experienced having their waist measured, so the notion of 'measuring round' is likely to be familiar, and they will usually have made headbands and bracelets at pre-school too.

Very young children just beginning school can be encouraged to think about area, although the term would not necessarily be used. By asking them how many prints they think will cover the paper, for example, you are introducing the concept of area. This can also be linked to tessellation and covering completely or with gaps. In technology, when cooking biscuits, for example, ask: *How many can we fit onto the baking tray? How many biscuits do you think we fit along the shorter edge of this oblong baking tray? If we fit four along this edge, how many will we need to cover the whole tray? If we use this larger cutter, will we be able to fit more or fewer onto the next tray?* Likewise in art activities, encourage the children to think about how many shapes they will be able to cut out from a sheet of paper, or how many shapes they will be able to fit on for their pattern: *Will Megan, who is using smaller squares, fit the same number onto her sheet of paper?*

BY THE END OF YR/P1 MOST CHILDREN SHOULD BE ABLE TO:

- compare lengths horizontally or vertically
- use vocabulary such as long, short, wide, narrow, thin etc in practical contexts.

BY THE END OF Y1/P2 MOST CHILDREN SHOULD BE ABLE TO:

- compare relative heights and lengths
- extend vocabulary to include words such as longer and longest
- estimate and then check relative measures using regular non-standard and simple standard units such as metres.

BY THE END OF Y2/P3 MOST CHILDREN SHOULD BE ABLE TO:

- measure and compare using metres and centimetres
- name some things longer/shorter than 1m/ 100cm, 10cm or 1cm
- suggest suitable measures: m or cm?
- estimate and measure 'round'
- start using calibrated measures.

MISCONCEPTIONS
TALL OR LONG?
Young children tend to use 'bigger' for every larger dimension. They need to know that when comparing the height of people we say, *Who is the tallest/ shortest?* However, when measuring teddies lying down we find their length: *Who has the longest/ shortest teddy?*

Lie a tower of interlocking cubes down to show that the length doesn't change, but the word we use does. Reassure the children that there is only one word for short/er, otherwise they will revert to 'smaller'.

IT'S ALL RELATIVE
If you put the 'longest' of two pencils next to a ruler it becomes 'shorter', or even 'the shortest'! Young children need to realize that size can be relative, but that the measurement of size is absolute: it's still a 15cm pencil, whether it's compared to a 10cm crayon or a 30cm ruler.

WHERE TO START MEASURING?
Most children find it easy to visually compare two lengths, however, it soon becomes necessary to be more accurate and the concept of a base line will need to be introduced. The children will quickly work out that they can 'choose' which teddy is taller by

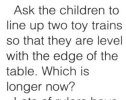

not lining up their feet!

Ask the children to line up two toy trains so that they are level with the edge of the table. Which is longer now?

Lots of rulers have the 0 inset from the end. At this stage, try to use 'infant' rulers that begin at 0, so that the end of the ruler is the beginning of the measure. Unfortunately, these rulers often have the numbers in the middle of the space. Check that the children are measuring from the beginning of the ruler and recording the measurement on the line after the number and not on the number. This is especially important when the children begin to measure and draw small lengths.

VERY NON-STANDARD
When you introduce the children to non-standard units move to 'regular' units as soon as possible: if you measure with pencils they must all be the same size. Use new ones! Otherwise, the result may be as shown in the illustration below.

Try to choose units that are a suitable size for the task. It is important to ask the children why they used fewer books than crayons. It is essential that they begin to realize that the larger the unit, the fewer will be required for measuring.

Children enjoy measuring with feet and hands. This is difficult unless they have several cut-out feet to use. The advantage of having several cut out is that they can be taped together to provide a more permanent record of the measurement. Try using all long feet and then all short feet for measuring the door. This makes for excellent discussion.

Check that the children measure from the beginning and to the end of the object and that the units are touching rather than overlapping or leaving gaps. Children do love counting to big numbers and overlapping can easily achieve this result!

ESTIMATE FIRST CUT TO MAKE ROOM?
Always ask the children to estimate before they measure: is their answer silly? They do not like estimating, but it is an essential to many areas of mathematics. An estimate should always begin with, 'I think it is about…'. It is a sensible guess. It often helps for you to say something silly, for example, 'I think the table is about two hands long.'

STANDARD MEASURES
CENTIMETRES ARE A VERY SHORT, FIDDLY MEASURE.
When standard measures are being introduced, it is easier to use a decimetre (1dm = 10cm length, such as a Dienes' 10-rod), ½m or a metre. The decimetre also reinforces work with multiples of 10.

MEASURING CURVES
The sequential motor control required to put a piece of string or paper or a tape measure along a curve to then measure against a ruler, if necessary, is very tricky and requires practice. (But it has been offered in the KS1 SATs.) Let the children try it in context on a large map.

LENGTH

THE TALLEST TEDDY

†† *4 to 6 children*
🕐 *About 10 minutes*

AIM
To use the correct vocabulary for comparing heights: taller than, tallest, shorter than, shortest, the same height as.

WHAT YOU WILL NEED
About four teddy bears of obviously different heights. You may need additional teddies for the extension activity.

WHAT TO DO
Stand the four teddies on a horizontal surface and ask:
● *Are these teddies all the same height?*
● *Who can tell me which teddy is the tallest? [Most young children will use 'big' and 'small' to describe height.]*
● *How do you know the brown teddy is the tallest?*
● *Which teddy is the shortest?*
● *How do you know?*

DISCUSSION QUESTIONS
● *Can you see a teddy that is taller than the yellow teddy?*
● *Does everyone agree?*
● *How do you know that the teddy with a red bow is taller than the yellow teddy?*

ASSESSMENT
Are the children able to use the correct vocabulary when comparing the teddies?

EXTENSION
Add more teddies and ask the children to find ones that are taller, shorter or in between. Point to a teddy and ask:
● *How many teddies are shorter than the teddy with a blue bow?*
● *If I mix up the teddies, can you put them back in order of height?*
● *Can you find two teddies that are exactly the same height?*

THE LONGEST TRAIN

†† *6 to 8 children*
🕐 *About 10 minutes*

AIM
To use the correct vocabulary for comparing lengths: longer than, longest, shorter than, shortest, the same length as.

WHAT YOU WILL NEED
Model trains: at least two engines, several carriages (of varying lengths if possible).

WHAT TO DO
Ask a child to make a train three carriages long. Ask the group:
● *Can anyone make a train that is shorter than Clare's train?*
● *Is this train shorter than Clare's train?*
● *How do you know? [If the carriages are the same length, the second train might have two carriages; or the children might be comparing the train lengths against each other.]*
It is important that the children learn to use a **baseline** for comparing lengths, so you may need to model this procedure using a carpet join, a tile line or a chalk line.

DISCUSSION QUESTIONS
● *Can anyone make a longer train?*
● *Is this train longer?*
● *How do you know?*
● *How can we make sure we are comparing accurately?*

ASSESSMENT
Note whether the children can say which of two trains is the longer or shorter. Can they explain how they know?

EXTENSION
Ask the children to arrange some toy vehicles in order of length. Check that they are using a baseline, and that they are able to answer these questions:
● *Which is the longest/shortest vehicle?*
● *How many vehicles are longer/shorter than the yellow car?*
● *How do you know?*

THE TWO TOWERS

†† *6 to 8 children*
🕑 *About 10 minutes*

AIM
To understand that we need more short units than long units to measure height.

WHAT YOU WILL NEED
Two sets of bricks in different sizes.

WHAT TO DO
Give two children a set each of bricks. Ask them to count out six bricks and make a tower from them. Before they start, ask the group:
● *Will both the towers be the same height?*
● *How do you know?*
When the two towers are built, ask:
● *Which tower is taller?*
● *How do you know?*

DISCUSSION QUESTIONS
● *Why are the towers not the same height?*
● *What do we need to do to make the towers the same height?*

ASSESSMENT
Ask various related questions to see whether the children can explain why the towers differ in height.

EXTENSION
Repeat the activity, using bricks of three different sizes.

ACROSS THE CLASSROOM

†† *Whole class or group*
🕑 *About 20 minutes*

AIM
To understand why we need a standard unit to measure distances.

WHAT YOU WILL NEED
A clear space between two walls that can be measured with footsteps.

WHAT TO DO
Ask the children:
● *How could we measure how far it is between the two walls?*

● *If we step across the floor, about how many steps will we take?*
● *Will it be the same number for everyone?*
● *Why/why not?*
Write down some estimates for the distance (in steps). Ask one child to stride across, then ask:
● *How many steps did Jack take?*
● *Do you think Poppy will take more steps, fewer steps or the same number of steps?*

DISCUSSION QUESTIONS
● *What could we use so that the answer was always the same? [Several strips of paper, exactly one child's step long.]*
● *How many strips do we need? How could we use them?*

ASSESSMENT
Note whether the children make sensible estimates of the distance in steps. Do they understand that the unit (step) used to measure the distance must stay the same during measurement? Are they also beginning to appreciate the need for a standard unit?

EXTENSION
The children can use a standard unit, such as a half-metre ruler, to estimate and measure other distances.

LENGTH

LENGTH

AROUND THE PE MAT

†† *The whole class (in a PE lesson)*
🕐 *About five minutes*

AIM
To begin to understand the concept of perimeter as the distance round an object.

WHAT YOU WILL NEED
Several PE mats (of varying sizes if possible), spread around the hall floor.

WHAT TO DO
Sit the class near one of the mats and ask: *How many children do you estimate will fit round this mat?* Ask them to test one of the estimates: that number of children should try to surround the mat. *Was our estimate correct? Do we need a greater number or a smaller number?* Look at a different-sized mat and repeat the questions.

DISCUSSION QUESTIONS
● *How many children are standing along the shorter length of the oblong?*
● *Are there the same number of children along both the shorter lengths of the oblong?*
● *Why/why not?*
Repeat for the longer side.
● *Would we need more or fewer children to surround the mat if we stretched out our hands?*
● *How can we measure the distance all the way round the mat? Do we need to count all the children standing round it? How else could we find the answer? This is called the* **perimeter**.

ASSESSMENT
Do the children understand that the perimeter of the mat is the distance around its edge? Are they using the correct vocabulary (**longer side, shorter side, opposite, all the way round**)?

EXTENSION
Ask the children to estimate and then measure the perimeters of other objects, using interlocking cubes or Compare Bears.

HOW TALL ARE YOU?

†† *6 to 10 children*
🕐 *About 30 minutes*

AIM
To use a standard measure (a decimetre) for measuring height.

WHAT YOU WILL NEED
Several decimetre lengths (Dienes and Multibase tens are a decimetre in length), long strips of card (about 120cm), adhesive.

WHAT TO DO
Tell the children that they are going to measure their heights using **decimetres**. Pass the decimetre lengths around, and ask the children to count the centimetres on them. Ask: *How many centimetres are there in a decimetre?*

Ask the group to arrange themselves in order of height. Use a marker to mark the height of one of the children on the wall, then ask:
● *Who can estimate how many decimetres tall Naayab might be?*
● *Who can measure how tall he is?*
The children should use the decimetre strips to measure. They could count centimetres in tens and 'extra ones' if finding the height of a child in centimetres. Record the height measurement on the board. Now ask:
● *Is anyone taller than Naayab?*
● *Is Raushan taller than Naayab? Check with the wall mark.*
● *How much taller do you think Raushan is than Naayab – more than a decimetre or less than a decimetre?*
Continue until all the children have been measured. Ask them to stick the appropriate number of decimetre strips to the wall, with their name and height attached on labels. They may like to stick faces onto the strips.

DISCUSSION QUESTIONS
● *How much taller is the tallest child than the shortest child?*
● *How many children are shorter than Naayab?*
● *How much taller is Mary than Tom?*

ASSESSMENT
Note whether the children are using appropriate vocabulary for measuring length (**taller than, shorter than, the same height as, shortest, tallest**). Can they make sensible estimates? Do they remember how many centimetres are in a decimetre?

VARIATION

Ask the children to lie down and to measure their length rather than their height. (This may be easier for them to manage.)

EXTENSIONS

● The children can predict and then measure how many decimetres are in a metre.
● They can measure their height in metres and centimetres using a metre ruler.
● They can investigate which measurement is greater: their height or the width of their outstretched arms.

PLASTICINE SNAKES

†† 8 children
⏰ About 30 minutes

AIM

To understand the concept of doubling and halving a length.

WHAT YOU WILL NEED

Plasticine and a ruler for each child (try to use infant rulers, which begin at zero).

WHAT TO DO

Ask the children to make a plasticine snake 20cm long and then check its length. Ask: *If you cut your snake in half, how long will it be?* When a child has made a prediction, let the group try and measure the half-snake. Now ask: *How long will the snake be if you cut it in half again?* Take a prediction, then let the group test it.

Now ask the children to make the 5cm snake into a 6cm snake (by rolling it a bit more) and to check the length with a ruler. Ask: *How long would the snake be now if you doubled its length?* You may want to ask them to halve the 6cm snake.

DISCUSSION QUESTIONS

● *If you double a snake that is 4cm long, how long will it be?*
● *If you halve this snake, how long will it be?*

ASSESSMENT

Note whether the children find half a length by measuring with the ruler. This is a more accurate method than folding the snake.

EXTENSIONS

● The children can practise cutting strips of card to the length of six interlocking cubes, then halving the lengths.
● They can complete photocopiable page 85 by drawing pictures that are double or half as long (or as high) as those provided.
● Older children can use square tiles to investigate dividing squares into halves and quarters (for example, half a square of four square tiles is an oblong of two square tiles).

MEASURING IN CENTIMETRES

†† Eight to ten children
⏰ About 20 minutes

AIM

To use a centimetre ruler accurately for measuring and drawing lines.

WHAT YOU WILL NEED

Infant rulers (starting at zero), photocopiable page 87, pencils.

WHAT TO DO

Give each child a ruler and a copy of page 87. Ask:
● *Can anyone tell me what each little space between two marks on the ruler measures?*
● *How long is your ruler in centimetres?*
● *Can you show me a measure of 6 centimetres on*

THE WHEEL GOES ROUND

†† *About 10 children*
🕐 *About 30 minutes*

AIM
To use measuring to solve a problem

WHAT YOU WILL NEED
A bicycle (or separate bicycle wheel), floor space, chalk, Scotch tape, a long strip of card, a metre ruler.

WHAT TO DO
This activity should follow the **group problem-solving** activity 'Making a headband'.
  Show the children a bicycle wheel. Ask them:
● *About how far do you think this wheel will travel along the floor when it goes round once?*
● *How will we know when the wheel has turned round exactly once?* [Mark the wheel with tape or use the valve.]
● *How can we show on the floor where the wheel started and finished turning?* [Mark the floor with tape or chalk.]
● *How could we record the distance travelled by the wheel without using a ruler?* [Cut a strip of paper.]

DISCUSSION QUESTIONS
● *Can you show me with your hands how far you think the wheel will travel?*
● *Do you think it will be longer or shorter than this metre ruler?*
● *Do you think it will be longer or shorter than the distance across the wheel? Why?*

ASSESSMENT
Note whether the children make sensible estimates of the length (that is, greater than the wheel's diameter), and whether they have good ideas for measuring it.

EXTENSION
The children can measure the diameter of the wheel with a strip of card, then find out how many of these strips will fit along the distance marked on the floor. They could investigate this with circular plates, lids and wheels.

the ruler with your fingers? [Check that they are starting at zero and ending at the 6 mark, not at the number 6.]
Repeat for other measures such as 9cm and 13cm.
  Now look at the sheet. Ask:
● *Without using your ruler, can you estimate how many centimetres long the first snake might be?*
● *Measure the first snake. How long is it?*
Check that all the children are measuring accurately before letting them complete the sheet independently.

DISCUSSION QUESTIONS
● *How long is the longest/shortest picture?*
● *Which picture is 5 centimetres taller than the first tree? How did you know?*

ASSESSMENT
● Note whether the children can make sensible estimates. Can they use the ruler correctly to measure?

EXTENSIONS
● Ask the children to draw a line 5 centimetres long, and then to draw another line 3 centimetres longer than the first.
● Ask them to measure curved lines (for example, the circumference of a circle) on paper by placing string along the line, then measuring the length of the straightened piece of string with a ruler.
● They can use photocopiable page 84 to practise measuring and comparing straight lines.

BIG FOOT, LITLE FOOT

†† About 10 children
🕐 About 30 minutes

AIM
To understand that you need more short units than long units to measure height.

WHAT YOU WILL NEED
Three pairs of shoes of obviously different sizes, Blu-tac, three sheets of different-coloured paper, pencils, scissors, photocopiable page 128.

WHAT TO DO
Hold up one of the largest pair of shoes and ask: *About how many of these shoes will we need to measure the height of the door?* Tell the children that trying to guess something sensibly in this way is called **estimating**. We use the word 'about' because we don't know the answer. You may want to record the children's estimates on the board.

Ask the children each to draw round and cut out one of the two largest shoes. They can use these with Blu-Tac to measure the door. Check that the shoe shapes are not being overlapped, and that spaces haven't been left between them. *How many shoe shapes have we used?* (You may need to allow a half-shoe as a measure.)

Hold up the middle-sized shoe and ask:
● *Will we need fewer or more of these shoe shapes to measure the door?*
● *Can you explain why?*
● *What about these small shoes?*
Ask the children to make middle-sized and small shoe shapes as before, and to measure the door with them. They can use the writing frame on page 128 to record their results.

DISCUSSION QUESTIONS
● *Which shoe have we used the greatest/smallest number of?*
● *Can you explain why?*
● *How many more middle-sized shoes have we used than small shoes?*

ASSESSMENT
By asking related questions, see whether the children can explain why you need more small shapes than large shapes to measure a door.

EXTENSION
● Tell the story of the Queen's Bed, asking the children to finish it for you. *The King wanted the Queen to have a new bed for her birthday. He sent for the carpenter and said: 'I need a bed six feet long and four feet wide for the Queen.' The carpenter went back to his workshop and asked his young apprentice to make the bed for the Queen. What do you think the King said when he saw the bed?* The children may know or guess that the young apprentice made a tiny bed – measuring with his feet! They could make brick beds using two sizes of shoe measure, then compare the beds.

HOW MANY BEARS?

†† 6 to 8 children
🕐 About 20 minutes

AIM
To understand that you need more short units than long units to measure length.

WHAT YOU WILL NEED
Blank paper, pencils, scissors, Compare Bears in three sizes.

WHAT TO DO
Show the children the three sets of plastic bears. Ask:
● *Which bears are the widest/narrowest?*
● *Which bears do you think you will need most/fewest of to measure the length of your foot?*
● *Why is that?*
● *What would be a good way to measure the length of your foot?*
Ask the children to draw round one of their shoes on paper, cut out the shape, stick it onto another sheet of paper and measure it using the three bears. They should record their results: '..... Daddy Bears long, ... Mummy Bears long and ..... Baby Bears long'.

LENGTH

DISCUSSION QUESTIONS
● Why did you use more small bears than middle-sized bears?
● How many more small bears than large bears did you use?

ASSESSMENT
Check that the children are measuring accurately with the bears, not overlapping or leaving gaps. They should fit the bears together so that they appear to be holding hands.

EXTENSION
Look at the measurements made using the small bears only. Ask the children:
● Who has the longest/shortest foot?
● How many of you have a foot that measures fewer than seven bears?
● How many bears longer/shorter is your foot than the longest/shortest foot in your group?

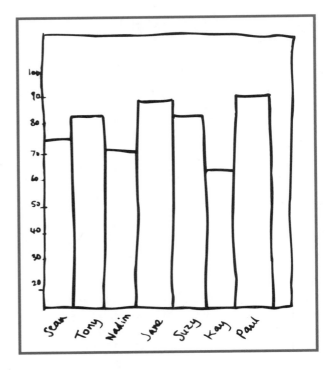

MAKING A HEADBAND

†† About half the class
🕐 About 30 minutes

AIM
To begin to understand perimeter as the distance round an object.

WHAT YOU WILL NEED
Long strips of thin card, scissors, plastic bears, coloured paper shapes (squares and oblongs), adhesive, self-adhesive labels.

WHAT TO DO
Ask the children to work in pairs, making card strips for headbands. They should make sure the strip is long enough, but do not need to worry if there is a slight overlap. When the strips have been cut and marked with each child's name, ask the children to arrange them in length order. Now ask:
● Who has the head with the largest/smallest perimeter?
● Can you measure your headband with the large bears to check?
Ask the children to decorate the headband with a repeating pattern, using the coloured paper shapes. Finally, they can stick the ends of the headband together with self-adhesive labels.

DISCUSSION QUESTIONS
● Do you think a bracelet would need a longer or shorter strip of card than this?
● Would a headband for me need to be longer or

shorter than this strip of card? Why?
● Will Sam's headband [the shortest] fit around Alice's head? Why/why not?

ASSESSMENT
Note whether the children are able to relate the lengths of the card strips to the perimeters of their heads.

EXTENSION
● The children can make a class 'head graph' by sticking their headband strips onto axes drawn on the wall (see figure).
● They can compare two perimeter measurements (for example, calf and ankle measurements) using card strips and plastic bears.

HALF A METRE

†† 8 to 10 children
🕐 About 10 minutes

AIM
To use a half-metre as a unit of measurement.

WHAT YOU WILL NEED
A metre ruler, several half-metre rulers (or one half-metre ruler, several metres of string and scissors), paper, pencils.

WHAT TO DO
Show the children a metre ruler and a half-metre ruler. Tell them that the longer ruler is a metre long. Ask:

**DEVELOPING SHAPE,
SPACE & MEASURES**

● *How many of the shorter rulers do you think will fit along the metre ruler?*
● *What do you think these shorter rulers could be called?*
Ask the children to work in pairs to find two things that are shorter and two things that are longer (or taller) than a half-metre ruler. They can use a half-metre ruler or an equivalent length of string for this, and write down what they find.

Ask the pairs to read out some of their suggestions, while other children check them with a half-metre ruler.

DISCUSSION QUESTIONS
● *Is it easier to find things longer or shorter than a half-metre ruler? Why?*

ASSESSMENT
Note whether the children:
● correctly identify items that are longer or shorter than a half-metre
● remember that there are two half-metres in a metre.

EXTENSIONS
● The children can estimate, then measure, how many pairs of scissors, shoes, pencils or decimetres will fit along a half-metre.
● They can estimate and measure bigger distances in half-metres, such as the length of the classroom or cloakroom, the height of a door or the length of a table.

BOX INVESTIGATION

†† *About 10 children, working in pairs*
🕐 *About 30 minutes*

AIM
To measure the dimensions of a box in centimetres.

WHAT YOU WILL NEED
A small box for each pair of children (perfume or tablet boxes are ideal), a centimetre ruler, photocopiable page 86.

WHAT TO DO
Give each pair a box and a copy of page 86. Use one box to talk through and demonstrate the activity on the sheet. Ask:
● *What shape is the box? [Cube or cuboid.]*
● *How many faces does it have?*
● *What shape are the faces?*
● *How high/wide/deep is the box?*
These ideas are difficult, and may need some explanation. Ask the children to imagine that the box is being displayed on the supermarket shelf. The **height** and **width** are easy to see. The term **depth** is confusing, as the children will have used it to talk about the vertical depth of a puddle, hole or bath. You will need to explain that 'depth' in this case refers to **how far back** the box goes. When they are clear about the vocabulary used, let the pairs complete the photocopiable sheet.

DISCUSSION QUESTIONS
● *Can you show me the square faces on your cuboid box?*
● *How do you know they are square?*
● *Who has the tallest box?*
● *How much taller is Ben's box than Megan's box?*
● *How many boxes are taller/shorter than 10 centimetres?*
● *How did you measure the width of your box?*

ASSESSMENT
Do the children use the ruler correctly? Do they remember which dimension they are measuring?

EXTENSIONS
● Ask the children to find the area of one of the faces, using centimetre square paper.
● Ask the children to find the volume of their box, using cubes of a suitable size.
● Ask the children to come together. Write their names and the height of each box on the board. Ask questions such as: *How many boxes are taller than William's box? What is the difference in height between Chloe's box and Jessica's box?*

LENGTH

MEASURING IN CENTIMETRES

■ Measure these lines carefully.

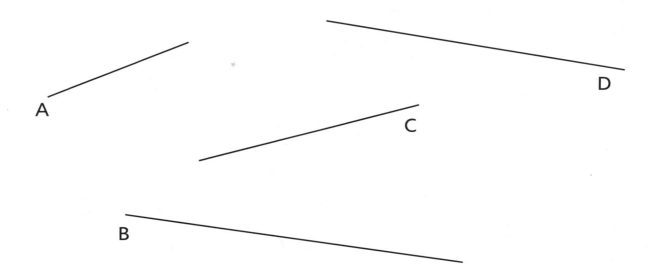

A is _____ centimetres long.

B is _____ centimetres long.

C is _____ centimetres long.

D is _____ centimetres long.

 Which is the longest line? _____

Which is the shortest line? _____

Which line is double the length of line A? _____

 Draw a line 2 centimetres longer than line B. Show your teacher.

SEE 'MEASURING IN CENTIMETRES', PAGE 79.

LENGTH

DOUBLING AND HALVING

This tree is _____ centimetres high.

■ Draw a tree double the height of this tree.

My tree is _____ centimetres high.

This snake is _____ centimetres long.

■ Draw a snake double the length of this snake.

My snake is _____ centimetres in length.

This pencil is _____ centimetres long.

■ Draw a pencil that is half the length of this pencil.

My pencil is _____ centimetres long.

 Do you think the doorway is double your height?
Tell a friend.

SEE 'PLASTICINE SNAKES', PAGE 79.

NAME

DATE

BOX INVESTIGATION

My box is a cube/cuboid.

It has _____ square faces and _____ oblong faces.

It is _____ centimetres high.

It is _____ centimetres wide.

It is _____ centimetres deep.

_____ has the widest box.

It is _____ centimetres wide.

It is _____ centimetres wider than my box.

 Imagine a cube box that is a metre high, wide and deep. Could you hide inside it?

SEE 'BOX INVESTIGATION', PAGE 83.

TREES, FISH AND SNAKES

■ How tall is this tree? _____ cm tall

■ Draw a tree that is 3 centimetres taller.

My tree is _____ cm tall.

■ How long is this fish? _____ cm long

■ Draw a fish that is 4cm shorter. My fish is _____ cm long.

■ What could you use to measure these snakes?

Snake A is _____cm long.

Snake B is _____cm long.

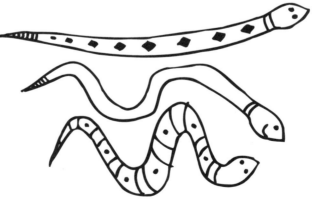

Snake C is _____cm long.

 Draw a snake for your friend to measure. Did you both do it the same way?

SEE 'MEASURING IN CENTIMETRES', PAGE 79.

DEVELOPING SHAPE,
SPACE & MEASURES

KEY IDEAS

- Practical experience to develop logic and understanding of comparing and ordering by quantity.
- Introduction to language of mass and capacity.
- Practical experience of estimation and measuring using non-standard measures and then simple standard units (g and kg, l and ml).
- Dispelling the myth that big things are heavy etc.

Mass and capacity are put together in this section because they both deal with how much something holds. Mass is usually applied to measures of dry quantities, and capacity to wet ones. It is essential that the children experience these activities using containers of many different shapes and sizes. They need to have play opportunities using sand and water before embarking on more formal activities. They will also need to use dry and wet fillers. Children will expect to fill more pots with a jugful of sand than an identical jug full of water, 'because sand is heavier'!

Young children often find it hard to dissociate size from weight and capacity. In these activities, it is suggested that, rather than holding objects to compare their weight, they are put into identical plastic carrier bags. (Of course, you must ensure that the children handle plastic bags with care.) The children will then be considering only the weight and not the appearance of the objects.

Likewise if they are comparing the weight of a 100g mass from the classroom scales with 100g bag of, say, dried beans, the children nearly always say the scale mass is heavier. Again, the carrier bags can help. (In fact, the force the mass applies to the child's hand will be greater per square centimetre than from the bag of dried beans because its weight is concentrated on a smaller area of the child's hand.)

Children need opportunities to 'play' with balances before using them more formally, when they will need to be taught how to use them. When finding out how many cubes will balance with an apple, for example, the children will need an adult to model and discuss how the problem can be solved. Many children will want to add cubes to both sides to make them balance. It may be tempting to balance ten cubes with ten cubes, but unless your balances have been carefully adjusted, I find that the children get some very odd answers, which can make the whole exercise meaningless.

Also, when making Plasticine or salt dough models the children will always (in my experience) make the model first and then use the balance. Use this for further discussion: *Could we do something with our Plasticine before making the snake to make the task easier?*

BY THE END OF YR/P1 MOST CHILDREN SHOULD BE ABLE TO:

- develop and use language related to comparison of quantity, including 'weight' and 'weighing'
- make comparisons between two objects
- use bucket balances and have experienced emptying and filling containers.

BY THE END OF Y1/P2 MOST CHILDREN SHOULD BE ABLE TO:

- make comparisons between three objects
- measure and estimate with regular non-standard measures.

BY THE END OF Y2/P3 MOST CHILDREN SHOULD BE ABLE TO:

- recognise g and kg, l and ml
- compare quantities relative to 1kg or 1l, that is, as heavier than… less than… etc
- measure practically using simple standard quantities, measuring to 1l/kg or 5l/kg
- start using calibrated measures.

COMMON MISCONCEPTIONS

BIG AND HEAVY

Many small children will say an object is light if they can pick it up and tend to associate the word 'heavy' with something that they cannot move. You will need to move the children on to more sensitive definitions.

Ask them to be precise: what *does* 'reeee...ally heavy' mean?

Likewise, it can be very confusing that weight does not always correlate with size. Small children are happy with 'big and heavy' or 'small and light', but they find it perplexing that everything doesn't fit neatly into these categories. If they try to compare weight by using their hands, the amount of their hand covered by the object will immediately prompt the answer that the one covering more is the heavier object.

Putting the objects into identical bags to compare them is the answer here.

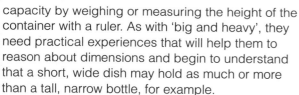

SHAPE AND CAPACITY

Young children expect to be able to measure capacity by weighing or measuring the height of the container with a ruler. As with 'big and heavy', they need practical experiences that will help them to reason about dimensions and begin to understand that a short, wide dish may hold as much or more than a tall, narrow bottle, for example.

WEIGHT AND MASS

Strictly speaking, mass is the correct term in this context as 'weight' refers to the force a certain mass applies. However, the word 'mass' is rarely used in real life and we talk commonly about 'weighing fruit at the supermarket' or 'knowing your weight', for example, and so the children need to be familiar with all this vocabulary and its correct application.

HALF FULL OR HALF EMPTY?

'Empty' is an easy word to understand – very young children become familiar with 'Gone!' as soon as they start to feed themselves! However, 'full' is commonly misapplied. A 'full cup' is rarely filled to the brim, but when we are measuring precisely that is what we mean. Worse still, is a beaker half full or half empty? By practical experience, the children need to come to realize that science and maths need us to be more exact with our use of words and meanings than is often the case in everyday life.

COMPARING MEASURES

Finding which of several containers holds the most is a difficult task. The children will usually reply by pointing to a container and saying : 'This one because it's taller/wider'. They need to experience pouring the contents of one into the other and explaining what has happened: 'This container has the least amount because it didn't fill the other container to the top. That container holds the most because the other container overflowed when I poured it in.'

Working with capacity is quite messy. It often helps to work with water and sand outside. When pouring from one container to another to compare mass or capacity, once they have poured the contents of one measure into another, young children often don't know what to do next – that is, to empty the smaller measure and refill it. You need to remember that this is not an everyday action. As adults we use calibrated measures and rarely pour from one thing to another, and while very small children may have had bathtime or nursery school water-play, they do not usually pour systematically between their toys.

USING REGULAR STANDARD UNITS

The move to standard units is sometimes difficult. Particularly when at home, the children will hear 'ounces', 'pints' and 'gallons' still used regularly. The children will need standard measures to experiment with: litres, pints and millilitres. Many will be familiar with medicine spoons which hold 5ml.

Grams are a very small unit of mass. We therefore need to establish a concept of balancing using other larger units first. When using grams the children will need to be able to count in 20s, 10s, 5s and 1s. They will also need to be taught how to work systematically with the weights. Demonstrate, asking: *Which weight shall I try first to find how many grams will balance with the apple? Does the apple balance? Do I need more grams or fewer?* (Let's say the apple is too heavy.) *What shall I do now?* (Try another 20g.) *Do I need more grams or fewer?* (Let's say the apple is now too light.) *What can we do now?* (Take out the 20g and put in 10g.)

Continue until the problem is solved. When children first begin these activities, they will need an adult to encourage systematic work.

DEVELOPING SHAPE, SPACE & MEASURES

MASS & CAPACITY

THE HEAVIER BAG

†† *Whole class or group*
🕐 *About 20 minutes*

AIM
To become familiar with the terms 'lighter', 'lighter than', 'heavier' and 'heavier than'.

WHAT YOU WILL NEED
Two plastic carrier bags of the same size and type, a large bag of potatoes, string, a marker pen. **NB Children should use plastic bags only with careful teacher supervision.**

WHAT TO DO
Before the children arrive, place one or two potatoes in one bag and the remainder in the other bag. Tie the bags closed. Ask one child to pick up a bag in each hand, then ask:
● *Which bag is the heavier?*
● *How do you know?*
● *Which bag is the lighter?*
Mark the heavier bag 'H' with a marker pen. Ask other children to hold the bags: do they all agree that the marked bag is the heavier? It is essential that they use the correct vocabulary ('lighter' and 'heavier') to describe the mass in the bags. You may like to encourage them to use their outstretched arms as a balance, asking: *Which arm goes down? Why?*

DISCUSSION QUESTIONS
● *Why does the heavier bag make your arm go down?*
● *Why is it heavier than the other bag?*

ASSESSMENT
Is each child able to say which bag is the heavier/ lighter and state the reason why?

EXTENSION
Ask the children what they could do to make the bags balance. They may say, 'You need to get more potatoes to put in the lighter bag,' or 'Put some of the potatoes from the heavier bag into the lighter bag.' Ask them to have a go at making the bags balance. As they will only be using their hands to balance, the results will be approximate.

PUT THE BAGS IN ORDER

†† *Up to 4 children*
🕐 *About 15 minutes*

AIM
To order different large masses by hand.

WHAT YOU WILL NEED
Four plastic carrier bags of the same size and type, a different mass of weights (apples, potatoes or stones) in each bag, string, marker pens in four colours. **NB Children should use plastic bags only with careful teacher supervision.**

WHAT TO DO
Tie the bags closed and mark each bag in a different colour. Ask the children to work together to arrange the bags in order of mass. You may need to simplify the task by offering three bags. Then ask:
● *Do you all agree on the order?*
● *Which bag is the heaviest?*

DISCUSSION QUESTIONS
● *Could you order the bags by lifting just one bag?*
● *Why not?*
● *How did you agree on the order?*

ASSESSMENT
Note whether all the children use appropriate strategies and language for this task. Are they able to order four bags, or did you need to offer three?

EXTENSIONS
● The children can order six bags.
● They can use a bucket balance (or similar) to check the order.

DEVELOPING SHAPE, SPACE & MEASURES

YOGHURT POTS

†† Up to 4 children
🕐 About 15 minutes

AIM
To order different small masses by hand.

WHAT YOU WILL NEED
Four identical yoghurt pots, each filled with a material of different mass (for example, rice, cornflakes, metal tacks, macaroni) and sealed with paper and sticky tape; felt-tipped pens; photocopiable page 128.

WHAT TO DO
Ask the children to order the pots in terms of their mass, and to find a way of recording the order on the pots so that they can remember without testing again. When they have established the order, reveal the contents. They should all observe that the containers are full to the top. Discuss the fact that the different masses of the pots are due to the different materials used to fill them, not how full they are. The children can use the writing frame on page 128 to record what they have found out.

DISCUSSION QUESTIONS
● *What will you need to do first?*
● *How will you mark the pots?*
● *Are all the containers full?*
● *Why does the mass vary?*

ASSESSMENT
Can the children work systematically to arrive at the order? Can they mark the pots appropriately? Can they explain how similar amounts can have different masses?

EXTENSION
The children can check the order with a balance.

MAKING QUEEN CAKES

†† About 6 children
🕐 About 1 hour

AIM
To use a balance to create a non-standard unit of mass.

WHAT YOU WILL NEED
Margarine, sugar, flour, sultanas, two eggs, a mixing bowl, a wooden spoon, a fork, cake cases, an oven.

WHAT TO DO
This would be a good activity to use after the children have encountered balancing (for example, through 'Balancing bears' on page 96). Explain to the children that it is traditional to use 'natural' units of mass in cooking – for example, an egg.

Work with the children to make cakes. Balance the

MASS & CAPACITY

sugar with the eggs, then balance the margarine with the eggs. Cream the sugar and margarine together in a bowl with a wooden spoon. Balance the flour with the eggs, but leave it in the balancing pan. Beat the two eggs into the mix with a fork, carefully fold in the sieved flour with a tablespoon, then add sultanas. Spoon the mix into cake cases on a baking tray and cook for 20 minutes at an appropriate level (190°C).

DISCUSSION QUESTIONS
● *How would you balance the sugar with two eggs?*
● *How many things have we balanced with two eggs?*
● *Which did we use more of, sugar or flour?*

ASSESSMENT
Can the children balance the different ingredients? Are they using appropriate language (**too light, too heavy, less of, more of**) when balancing?

VARIATION
Work through another recipe together using this method of balancing with one ingredient.

A KILOGRAM

†† *Whole class or group (about 10 children)*
🕐 *About 20 minutes*

AIMS
To use the kilogram as a standard unit of mass. To understand that shape and size do not specify mass.

WHAT YOU WILL NEED
A bucket balance, a 1kg weight, 1kg of pasta, 1kg of rice, two plastic bags of the same size and type. **NB Children should use plastic bags only with careful teacher supervision.**

WHAT TO DO
Hold up the rice and the pasta in their original containers (without showing the weights), then pour them into separate plastic bags. Ask several children to hold the bags and tell you which is the heavier.

Then ask the children what they think will happen when you place the bags in the two buckets of the balance. Demonstrate. Can they explain what has happened?

Explain that each bag contains a kilogram – one of pasta and one of rice. Show the children the 1kg weight and pass it round in a bag. Repeat with the rice.

DISCUSSION QUESTIONS
● *What do you think will happen when we put the kilogram in one bucket and the pasta in the other?*
● *How much does the rice weigh?*
● *How can this can be proved? Show me.*

ASSESSMENT
Note whether the children are using the correct vocabulary (**heavier, lighter**) for mass. Are they beginning to recognize that size is not necessarily an indication of the mass of an object?

EXTENSIONS
● Ask the children to find books, bricks, stones or shoes to balance a 1kg weight.
● Go on to the **group problem-solving** activity 'A kilogram of sand' (page 97).

USING GRAMS

†† *Up to 10 children, working in pairs*
🕐 *About 20 minutes*

AIM
To use grams as a standard unit of mass.

WHAT YOU WILL NEED
A balance for each pair, a set of gram weights (20g, 10g, 5g and 1g), small classroom objects or groups of objects (eg a ruler, four pencils, six rubbers). You may want to show the children a food package that displays the mass in grams.

WHAT TO DO
Pass round the weights for the children to observe. Then ask:
● *Do you think they are all the same weight?*
● *Why/why not?*
● *Is there anything written on them that could help us to know which ones are heavier?*
● *Can you put them in order?*
● *What do you think the 'g' stands for? [You may need to say that it is the number of grams.]*
Now ask the children to find the masses of several small objects or groups of objects (see above). As they work, ask the pairs:
● *Is it better to start weighing with the 20g or the 1g? [20g]*
● *Why? [It will usually save time.]*
● *What will you do if the 20g is too heavy/too light?*

DISCUSSION QUESTIONS
See above.

ASSESSMENT
Note whether the children use the weights in a systematic way. Can they explain how they have approached the task?

EXTENSIONS
● The children can make Plasticine or salt dough snakes or cats to balance with 20g, using trial and improvement.
● They can use photocopiable page 102 to relate grams to kilograms (1kg = 1000g).

 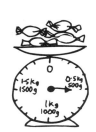 

FULL OR EMPTY?

†† *About 6 children*
🕐 *About 10 minutes*

AIM
To use and understand the words 'full' and 'empty'.

WHAT YOU WILL NEED
Water, sand, rice, pasta, small objects in the classroom, a variety of containers.

WHAT TO DO
Ask the children to choose a container and to **fill it** with water, then ask them to **empty** the container. Repeat, using a variety of other fillers to broaden the children's experience of these concepts. When they are using dry materials, they will need to level off the surface to show that the container is full. Explain that we sometimes use these terms inexactly – for example, a truly **full** cup of tea would be dangerous to drink!

DISCUSSION QUESTIONS
● *Is the container full of water?*
● *Will it hold more?*
● *How will you know when the container is full of*

DEVELOPING SHAPE, SPACE & MEASURES

sand? [It must level off at the top of the container.]
● *Is it empty? How do you know?*

ASSESSMENT

Note whether the children confidently fill and empty their containers and use the appropriate language (**full, empty**).

EXTENSION

Do the children get the same results when using other fillers? This will help them to recognize that capacity and mass are different things.

WHICH HOLDS MORE?

†† *About 8 children, working in pairs*
⏰ *About 15 minutes*

AIM

To compare the capacities of different containers.

WHAT YOU WILL NEED

Two containers of obviously different capacities, a metal tray (to hold drips), a jug of water large enough to fill both containers, a funnel, photocopiable page 128.

WHAT TO DO

Ask the children:
● *Which container do you think will hold more water?*

● *Why do you think that?*
● *How can we use the water to find out which container holds more? Show me.*
This is often difficult. You may need to ask several children before you find a correct method. Common incorrect methods are:
● filling both containers
● filling one container, then emptying it back into the jug.
You may need to lead the children by asking:
● *Which container do you think holds less (has the smaller capacity)?*
● *Can you fill it with water?*
● *What will happen if you pour the water into the other container?*
  Give each pair of children two containers and ask them to find out which container holds more. They can record their work using the writing frame on page 128.

DISCUSSION QUESTIONS

See above.

ASSESSMENT

Can the children say which container holds more, and demonstrate how to prove it? Do they use appropriate vocabulary such as 'overflows', 'does not fill it up to the brim', 'there is still space at the top'?

EXTENSION

● The children can explore some containers that have different shapes, but may have the same capacity.

SMALL CONTAINERS

†† *About 6 children*
🕐 *About 15 minutes*

AIMS
To know that small amounts of liquids are usually measured in millilitres (ml). To know that there are 1000ml in a litre.

WHAT YOU WILL NEED
A supply of commercial liquid containers (either sealed or empty) with labels stating their capacity.

WHAT TO DO
Ask the children:
● *How much does each bottle or carton contain?*
● *Which one holds the most/least?*
● *Can you order these containers by capacity?*
● *If a litre is 1000ml, is there a container here that holds exactly half a litre? How do you know?*

DISCUSSION QUESTIONS
● *Were you surprised at the capacity of any of the containers?*
● *How could you explain the capacity being less than you'd expected? [Thick bottoms or concave sides.]*
● *Why might they have been made this way? [For greater strength – or to mislead the buyer.]*

ASSESSMENT
Are the children able to read and order the printed numbers? Can they relate millilitres to litres?

EXTENSION
Wash out a collection of different-sized bottles. Can the children fill two, three, four or five bottles with water so that each group holds a litre? They can use the printed capacity values or pour from a litre jug.

LUNCHTIME DRINKING

†† *The whole class*
🕐 *About 20 minutes (after lunch)*

AIM
To add up measures of capacity in a practical context.

WHAT YOU WILL NEED
Several buckets and litre measures, a funnel, photocopiable page 128.

WHAT TO DO
Before lunch, ask the children to keep the empty drinks cans, bottles and cartons they use at lunchtime. Tell them that they are going to find out how much they have drunk at lunchtime. After lunch, ask the children to tell you how many millilitres their empty containers held. Now ask them to fill their containers with water, then empty them into a bucket. Go on to another bucket if the first is filled. When they have all emptied their containers, ask:
● *How many buckets have we filled?*
● *How many litres do you think each bucket holds?*
● *How could we find out?*
The children should now use litre measures to find the capacity of each bucket. Supervise this work. Finally, calculate together how much the whole class drank at lunchtime. The children can record and reflect on this investigation, using the writing frame on page 128.

DISCUSSION
● *If this carton holds 200ml, how many would we need to make a litre?*
● *If this bucket holds 5 litres, how much will four buckets hold?*
● *How many litres have we drunk this lunchtime? How do you know?*

ASSESSMENT
Do the children make sensible estimates? Can they measure the contents of the buckets in litres?

VARIATION
Group the used containers into 1 litre batches before the activity.

HOW MANY BEARS?

†† *Up to 10 children, working in pairs*
🕐 *About 15 minutes*

AIM
To use a pan balance correctly.

WHAT YOU WILL NEED
A pan balance and a potato (not too large) for each pair, Compare Bears (in three sizes), photocopiable page 103.

WHAT TO DO
Introduce the equipment and ask the group: *What do you think will happen when you put your potato in one of the balancing pans? Why?* Ask each pair to try and see. Now ask:
● *How can we make it balance with the daddy bears?*
● *How many do you think we will need?*
● *Will everyone need the same amount? Why/why not?*
Ask the pairs to do this. You may want to show with your arms what happens when the pans balance. If some pairs are unable to achieve a complete balance with daddy bears, help them to improvise (for example, by adding one baby bear). When all

the potatoes are balanced, ask:
● *How can you tell your potato is balanced? [The pointer is touching the line.]*
● *How many daddy bears did you need?*
● *Did we all use the same number? Why/why not?*
● *Do you think we will use fewer or more mummy bears, or the same number? Why?*
● *About how many will you need?*
Try this, then repeat with baby bears.

DISCUSSION QUESTIONS
● *What do you need to do to make the pans balance?*
● *Which side is too heavy?*
● *What will you need to do to make them balance now?*

ASSESSMENT
Note whether the children make reasonable estimates. Do they know that the number needed will be larger if the bears have a smaller mass? Are they using vocabulary appropriate to the task (**too heavy, too light, balance, add more, take away**)?

Check that the children are not adding bears to the potato in an attempt to make the pans balance. In this situation, they need to remove bears from the bears pan.

EXTENSION
Repeat with another vegetable, using interlocking cubes (in ones, twos or threes) as units of mass.

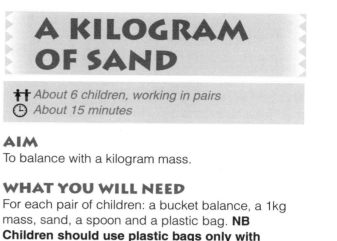

A KILOGRAM OF SAND

†† *About 6 children, working in pairs*
🕐 *About 15 minutes*

AIM
To balance with a kilogram mass.

WHAT YOU WILL NEED
For each pair of children: a bucket balance, a 1kg mass, sand, a spoon and a plastic bag. **NB Children should use plastic bags only with careful teacher supervision.**

WHAT TO DO
Ask each pair to fill the bag carefully with sand until it balances with a kilogram mass.

DISCUSSION QUESTIONS
● *Does your bag balance the kilogram?*
● *How do you know?*
● *Is it too heavy or too light?*
● *What will you need to do to make it balance?*

ASSESSMENT
Do the children add or take away sand as necessary to make the bag balance? Are they using the correct vocabulary (see previous activity) for the task?

EXTENSION
The children can use 1kg to weigh out apples, potatoes or carrots, where they need to select items carefully to achieve a balance.

A PLASTICINE SNAKE

†† *Up to 10 children, working in pairs.*
🕐 *15 minutes*

AIMS
To balance objects. To use the correct vocabulary (**heavier, lighter, balance, add, take away**).

WHAT YOU WILL NEED
A balance for each pair of children, Plasticine, interlocking cubes.

WHAT TO DO
Ask each pair to make a Plasticine snake that will balance with 15 cubes. Most children will make an extremely long snake before attempting to use the balance. This makes an excellent discussion point for later: length by itself does not specify mass.

DISCUSSION QUESTIONS
● *Is your snake too heavy or too light?*
● *What will you need to do to make it balance? [If it is too light, some children will roll it out longer rather than add more Plasticine. If it is too heavy, they may want to add more cubes.]*
● *Do all the snakes balance with 15 cubes?*
● *Are all the snakes the same length? Why/why not?*
● *How can we make sure our snake will balance before we start to roll it out?*

ASSESSMENT
Do all the children know how to achieve a balance? Are they all using the correct vocabulary (see Aims) for the task?

EXTENSION
The children can make snakes to the same length as before, but to balance with 20 cubes.

ORDER THE BOXES

†† *4 children*
🕐 *About 10 minutes*

AIMS
To compare the masses of objects by hand. To read measures of mass in grams.

WHAT YOU WILL NEED
Six sealed containers (boxes or cartons) with their mass (in grams) printed on them. Cover up these numbers with Post-it notes initially.

WHAT TO DO
Ask the children to feel the masses of the containers and try to put them in order. When the order has been agreed, ask the children to peel off the labels

MASS & CAPACITY

MASS & CAPACITY

and read out the masses. Note that using cardboard containers ensures that the mass of the contents (printed on the label) will be close to the mass of the whole package.

DISCUSSION QUESTIONS
● *Do we all agree that this box is the heaviest?*
● *Is the biggest box the heaviest? How do you know?*
● *Was our order correct? How do we know?*
● *Did we have any surprises? Why/why not?*

ASSESSMENT
Note whether the children used suitable vocabulary (see previous activities) and strategies for solving the problem. A good strategy would be to work systematically through the boxes.

EXTENSION
The children can sort packages (with the labels covered up) into sets: 'more than 100g' and 'less than 100g'.

FILL THE BOXES

†† *About 8 children, working in pairs*
🕑 *About 15 minutes*

AIM
To fill a box to a given mass.

WHAT YOU WILL NEED
For each pair: an empty food box (with a label), sand, a spoon, gram weights (1g, 5g, 10g and 50g), a balance. Strengthen the boxes with adhesive tape to prevent leakage.

WHAT TO DO
Ask the children to read the mass on each box. Discuss the relative masses, then ask the pairs to fill each box so that it has the mass stated on the label. Encourage them to think through their method before they start.

DISCUSSION QUESTIONS
● *Which box will be the heaviest/lightest? How do you know?*
● *Does the largest box have the greatest mass? Why/why not?*
● *What weights can you use to make up the number on your box?*
● *How many grams of sand will you need?*
● *Is your box too heavy or too light?*
● *What will you need to do to make your box balance the weights?*
● *Have you filled your box with sand? Why do you think that is?*

ASSESSMENT
Do the children use the correct number of weights to match the stated mass? Do they know what to do if the box becomes too heavy? Do they successfully balance the box with the weights?

EXTENSION
Ask the children to make the box 20g heavier or lighter than the mass stated on the packet, and to write the new mass on the box.

HALF FULL

†† *About 8 children, working in pairs*
🕑 *About 20 minutes*

AIM
To fill or empty a container to approximately half full.

WHAT YOU WILL NEED
A variety of plastic containers, water, funnels, self-adhesive labels. You may prefer to use fairly straight-sided containers.

WHAT TO DO
This activity should follow the **teacher-directed activities** 'Full or empty?' (page 93) and 'Which holds more?' (page 94). Give each pair a container. Ask the children to pour water into their containers

until they are half full, then mark the level with a label.

DISCUSSION QUESTIONS
● *Have all the labels been put at half full? How do you know? What does 'half full' mean?*
● *If the container is full, would you prefer the top half or the bottom half? Why?*

ASSESSMENT
Do the children understand what is meant by 'half full'?

EXTENSION
The children can use yoghurt pots to measure the capacity of a container in order to half-fill it accurately. This is particularly important for containers that taper into a neck, since the half-full level is difficult to judge by eye.

HOW MANY CUPS?

✝✝ *About 6 children, working in pairs*
🕐 *About 15 minutes*

AIM
To measure capacity using a regular non-standard unit.

WHAT YOU WILL NEED
A plastic or metal teapot and several identical plastic beakers (or yoghurt pots) for each pair, another set for demonstration, water. You may want to use teapots that vary in capacity.

WHAT TO DO
Fill a teapot with water. Hold up a plastic beaker and ask: *How many of these do you think the teapot will fill?* Count out an agreed estimate. Ask a child to start filling the beakers. Discuss the result:
● *How many beakers have we filled?*
● *Is this more or fewer than our estimate?*
● *Does the teapot hold exactly six beakers full of water?*
Ask the children to work in pairs to estimate, then find out, the capacity of the teapots.

DISCUSSION QUESTIONS
● *Did you fill the beakers to the brim?*
● *Do all the teapots hold the same number of beakers?*
● *Why/why not?*
● *What would happen if we filled these [smaller] yoghurt pots from the teapot? Why? Who can show us?*

ASSESSMENT
Note whether the children fill the beakers consistently and sensibly, making the beaker a regular unit of capacity. Do they make sensible estimates?

EXTENSIONS
● The children can compare how many cups and how many mugs the same teapot will fill, recording on photocopiable page 104. Can they explain the difference in the number?
● They can estimate, then find out, how many yoghurt pots full of water are needed to fill a jug.

A LITRE OF WATER

✝✝ *About 8 children, working in pairs*
🕐 *At least 20 minutes*

AIM
To become familiar with a litre as a standard measure.

WHAT YOU WILL NEED
Several empty litre containers (in different shapes if possible), a collection of yoghurt pots in two sizes,

**DEVELOPING SHAPE,
SPACE & MEASURES**

water, a tray (to hold the drips), photocopiable page 105.

WHAT TO DO

You may prefer to split this activity into two sessions, one for the demonstration and one for investigation and recording.

Show the children the empty containers and ask:
● *Which one do you think holds the most/least?*
● *How could we find out?*

You may need to establish that they all hold 1 litre by pouring water from a measuring jug into each bottle. Most litre bottles hold slightly more than a litre to allow for expansion; you may want to show them an unopened bottle to demonstrate this point.

Once it has been established that each container holds 1 litre, ask:
● *How many of these large yoghurt pots can we fill with the litre?*
● *What about these smaller yoghurt pots: will it be the same number, fewer or more? Why?*

Ask the children to work in pairs with a litre container and two sets of yoghurt pots, using a copy of page 105 to record and explain their results.

DISCUSSION QUESTIONS

● *Did the litre fill the same number of pots both times?*
● *Did you use more or fewer of the large pots? Why?*

ASSESSMENT

Note whether the children worked systematically to obtain consistent results, recorded them accurately and gave a correct explanation.

VARIATION

The children could reverse the procedure to find out how many pots will fill the litre bottle.

HOW FAR UP?

†† *Up to 10 children, working in pairs*
🕐 *About 20 minutes*

AIM

To understand that the same volume of liquid in different-shaped containers may have different levels.

WHAT YOU WILL NEED

For five pairs: five identical mugs, different-shaped or different-sized containers, funnels, strips of self-adhesive labels and copies of photocopiable page 128; water.

WHAT TO DO

Ask the children to look at a large container and estimate how far up the level will be if you pour in one mugful of water. Ask a child to fill a mug and pour it into the container, being careful not to spill any. Now ask:
● *Will a mugful of water reach the same level in all these containers?*
● *Why/why not?*

Ask each pair to estimate and then find the level of a mugful of water in a container. They can use labels to mark their estimate and result. They can use the writing frame on page 128 to record their investigation.

DISCUSSION QUESTIONS

● *In which container has the level come up highest/ lowest?*
● *Why do you think that is?*
● *Which container has the most water in it?*
● *How do you know?*

ASSESSMENT

Do all the children understand why the level is different for different containers, even though the quantity of water is the same?

EXTENSION

The children can use a measured or marked container (such as one holding exactly 40ml) to fill the larger container. What do they observe about the results?

FILL THE EGGCUP WITH WATER

†† *About 10 children, working in pairs*
⏱ *About 20 minutes*

AIM
To begin to recognize a 5ml spoon as a standard measure.

WHAT YOU WILL NEED
A 5ml plastic spoon and an eggcup for each pair, water, photocopiable page 106. The eggcups should be of different sizes.

WHAT TO DO
Ask the children:
● *How many millilitres does your spoon hold? [This will usually be marked on the spoon.]*
● *How many spoonfuls of water do you think you will need to fill the eggcup?*
● *How many millilitres do you think you will need to fill the eggcup?*
Ask the children to record their results on the photocopiable sheet.

DISCUSSION QUESTIONS
● *Which is easier, counting the spoons or the millilitres?*
● *When is a spoonful a useful unit for measuring amounts?*

ASSESSMENT
Do the children count accurately in fives? Do they understand the idea of using a 5ml unit of capacity as a measure?

EXTENSION
The children can use spoons with different capacities to measure the capacities of cups or yoghurt pots.

A CALIBRATED CONTAINER

†† *About 10 children, working in pairs*
⏱ *About 20 minutes*

AIM
To calibrate a container with units of capacity.

WHAT YOU WILL NEED
For each pair: a plastic 1 litre bottle, a yoghurt pot, a funnel, self-adhesive paper strips.

WHAT TO DO
Ask the children to pour a yoghurt potful of water carefully into the litre bottle, using a funnel. They should mark the level of water clearly with a paper strip. Ask them to continue filling the bottle with the pot, marking each new level, until the bottle is full. Tell them that the regular marks on the side of the bottle are called **calibrations**, and discuss why they are useful.

DISCUSSION QUESTIONS
● *Is your yoghurt pot full each time you pour it into the bottle?*
● *About how many potfuls do you think the litre bottle will hold?*
● *Will all the bottles have the same number of marks? Why/why not?*
● *Why is it useful to have a bottle marked like this?*

ASSESSMENT
Do the children understand that each calibration represents a potful of water?

EXTENSION
Ask the children to fill their calibrated containers to various levels. Now explain that there are 1000ml in a litre, and provide containers calibrated with standard units. Ask the children to fill these to various levels. More able children could go on to complete photocopiable page 107.

MASS & CAPACITY

HOW HEAVY ARE THESE?

■ How heavy are the apples?

_____ kilograms

■ The potatoes weigh

_____

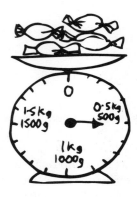

■ How heavy are the sweets?

_____

■ Which is the heaviest bag? _____

How much does it weigh? _____

■ Which is the lightest bag? _____

How much does it weigh? _____

 If the pointer on each scale moved all the way round to the 0, how heavy would the mass on top be? Tell your teacher.

SEE 'USING GRAMS', PAGE 93.

NAME _____   DATE _____

BALANCE THE BEARS

■ How many plastic bears will balance with the potato?

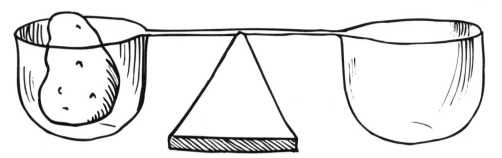

The potato balances with _____ Daddy bears.

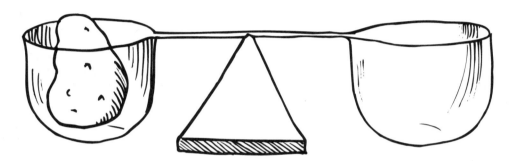

The potato balances with _____ Mummy bears.

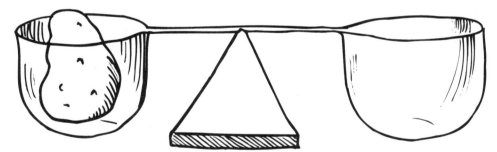

The potato balances with _____ Baby bears.

■ We used more _____ bears
because they are heavier/lighter.

 Did you use more or fewer Daddy bears than
Mummy or Baby bears? Why? Tell your teacher.

SEE 'HOW MANY BEARS?', PAGE 96.

NAME _____ **DATE** _____

TEATIME MEASURES

■ The teapot fills _____ cups.

■ Colour how many cups you filled.

■ Colour how many mugs you filled.

■ The teapot fills _____ mugs.

 Did you fill more cups or mugs? Why? Tell a friend.

SEE 'HOW MANY CUPS?', PAGE 99.

MASS & CAPACITY

NAME _____   **DATE** _____

HOW MANY POTS?

■ Colour how many pots you used to fill the litre bottle.

■ I used _____ small yoghurt pots to fill the litre bottle.

■ I used _____ large yoghurt pots to fill the litre bottle.

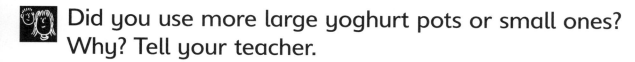 Did you use more large yoghurt pots or small ones? Why? Tell your teacher.

SEE 'A LITRE OF WATER', PAGE 99.

NAME _____   DATE _____

HOW MANY SPOONS?

■ Colour the number of 5ml spoons that you used to fill the eggcup.

■ I used _____ spoons to fill the eggcup.

■ I counted the ml in fives. There is _____ml of water in the eggcup.

 Whose eggcup held the most water? _____

How much did it hold? _____ml

SEE 'FILL THE EGGCUP', PAGE 101.

MASS & CAPACITY

FILL IT UP!

There is _____ of water in this container.

■ Colour in this container to fill it up to 600ml.

■ Colour in this container to fill it up to 750ml.

■ How much water is in this container? _____

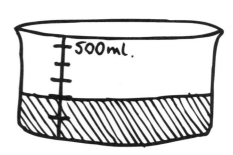

 Which container has the least amount of water in it? Tell your teacher.

SEE 'A CALIBRATED CONTAINER', PAGE 101.

DEVELOPING SHAPE,
SPACE & MEASURES

KEY IDEAS

- Familiarity with the vocabulary needed for telling the time and for longer periods such as the names of the days and months.
- Ordering events.
- Comparing the lengths of events.
- Beginning to tell the time using analogue and digital clocks.
- Starting to estimate the passage of time.

Time is measured in many different units. It is therefore essential that these different measures are firmly established before attempting to tell the time using a clock. Children will usually know when they start school that their age is measured in years. Many will be able, with help, to work out the year of their birth. From a fairly early age, they are aware of significant parts of the day: 'I get dressed in the morning. Breakfast is my first meal of the day. I go to bed after tea. Mostly, it is dark at bedtime.' Problems do arise in summer: 'It can't be bedtime because it is still light!'

Many children arrive in school knowing the sequence of the days of the week and are beginning to associate some days with special events. For example, 'We go swimming on Thursday', or 'Grandma comes for tea on Sunday'.

Many will know their birthday months and be able to associate this with the seasons or special dates. For example, 'My birthday is in December, just before Christmas.' Others will know the special event, but not the month. Be aware of religious differences with respect to celebrations.

With learning to 'tell the time', fascination helps to motivate – if the children are not interested it can be very hard for them to learn.

BY THE END OF YR/P1 MOST CHILDREN SHOULD BE ABLE TO:

- use the language of time and sequencing common in everyday speech
- sequence events (this also relates to giving instructions – 'Key ideas' for 'Position and direction' section on page 44)
- have a sense of time being measured, but not necessarily with standard units, for example, 'By a count of 10...'
- understand some significant times, for example, home time.

BY THE END OF Y1/P2 MOST CHILDREN SHOULD BE ABLE TO:

- use the language of 'how long?' and comparison, eg faster or slower;
- tell you that 7 days = 1 week and 24 hours = 1 day
- tell 'o'clock' and 'half past' times on an analogue clock
- measure time with a sand timer, or by '...o'clocks'.

BY THE END OF Y2/P3 MOST CHILDREN SHOULD BE ABLE TO:

- extend their vocabulary to include minutes, and possibly seconds
- tell you that 1 hour = 60 minutes, and probably that 1 minute = 60 seconds
- name some significant times for themselves, for example, home time
- use analogue and digital time, including 'quarter to/past'
- suggest suitable measures for timing, for example, how long it takes to walk home, and how to measure 10 minutes or 1 hour.

COMMON MISCONCEPTIONS

YESTERDAY

Today and tomorrow seem to be understood by most children, but yesterday is problematic. Using the past tense 'was' appears to add to the confusion. It helps to associate yesterday with something significant, for example, 'Can you remember what we did/where we went yesterday?'

Many Reception/Primary 1 children will talk about 'sleeps to' the next event, rather than days. This is because the night seems to be a more significant break point to them.

HAPPY HOUR

Telling the time using a clock is extremely difficult and easily misunderstood by some children. If a child is especially interested in a particular television programme, for example, they may be more interested in telling the time. For other children, who are equally intelligent, telling the time holds no fascination or interest.

It is unhelpful that the numbers on a clock face only relate to the hours and that the minute times are calculated using the dots in between. Children need to be able to differentiate between the hands on the clock before being able to tell the time. This is a major stumbling block for the majority.

It is vital to discuss the clock informally many times in a day, long before you introduce the teaching of telling the time. Point to the clock and say, for example: *It is two more minutes before you go home at 3 o'clock.* Count the two dots, point to the minute hand and say: *The minute hand will need to move one, two minutes before 3 o'clock. The hour hand will then be exactly on the three.*

Try: *You have 5 more minutes to finish your work,* and place a little Blu-Tack in the position on the clock so that the children will be aware that the minute hand has travelled five dots.

I usually encourage the children to observe the faster movement of the minute hand while reading a story, changing for PE etc. It is easy to set challenges for three or four minutes. Count four dots and place a sticker and ask: *Can we tidy up in 4 minutes? Can you change for PE in 4 minutes? Can you all put your homework in your book bag in 2 minutes?* It may help with differentiation to say, *Remember the minute hand is long and thin, it travels faster than the short, fatter hour hand!*
The times '…past' up to half-past are fairly easy. The times towards the next hour are especially difficult. Calculating 'in ten minutes time' can also be confusing because you are now calculating ten minutes anywhere on the clock face.

A digital clock is read differently from an analogue clock. Do not introduce digital time beyond 12.00 at Key Stage 1: the 24-hour clock is too difficult a concept at this stage.

HOW LONG, NOW?

Estimating the passing of time is also very difficult. Time passes so much quicker when you are having fun, not in a rush and on a sunny day! How often in a minute have we all looked at our watches while waiting in the cold and wet for a bus?

As adults we often say we will 'help in a second/ minute' and these times will have nothing at all to do with the passage of time. Precise use of language is the problem – and the solution – here.

TIME

DAYS OF THE WEEK

†† *Whole class*
🕐 *About 10 minutes*

AIM
To know the days of the week in the correct order.

WHAT YOU NEED
A chart showing the days of the week in order.

WHAT TO DO
Pin up a list of the days of the week and read through it in unison. Now ask the children to sit in a circle. Ask them: *What day is it today?* (For example, Wednesday.) Explain that they are all going to say the days together, but when they say 'Wednesday' they should clap their hands (or stand up and sit down). Go through the days several times in this way. Repeat for other days, including a 'weekend day' (Saturday or Sunday).

DISCUSSION QUESTIONS
● *Which day comes after Wednesday?*
● *Which day comes before Wednesday?*
● *Which are the weekend days?*
● *Which day do we go swimming?*

ASSESSMENT
Can the children read out the days of the week? Can they then recall and say the days of the week in order?

EXTENSION
Ask the children to stand in a circle and take turns to say a day of the week, going round the circle. When they are familiar with this, play an elimination game. Choose a day (perhaps the day it is) and tell the children they have to sit down if they say this day. This is an excellent game for ensuring that all the children know the days of the week. Children who find it difficult should be positioned near a supportive child.

TODAY, TOMORROW, YESTERDAY

†† *Whole class*
🕐 *About 10 minutes*

AIM
To read a calendar and know the date for each day.

WHAT YOU NEED
A large monthly calendar grid (see illustration), displayed with small number cards 1–31 pinned around it.

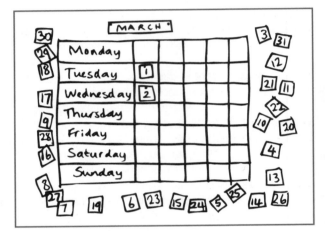

WHAT TO DO
At the start of each month, take the numbers off the grid and label the grid with the new month. Ask:
● *Who can read the days down the side of the grid?*
● *What day is it today?*
● *What date are you going to pin up?*
● *Which square will the date go in?*

DISCUSSION QUESTIONS
● *What day of the week will it be tomorrow?*
● *What date will it be?*
● *What date will it be on Saturday?*
● *Why do you think we have only used 30 days this month, when there are 31 on the grid?*
● *Why don't all the months begin on a Monday?*

ASSESSMENT
Are the children able to say the date (eg 'Today is Monday the 2nd of June')? Ask different children on different days.

EXTENSION
Combine this activity with a weather chart by making each date space larger (oblong) and asking the children to place weather symbols (see illustration).

BIRTHDAY MONTHS

†† Whole class
⏰ About 10 minutes

AIMS
To know the months of the year in the correct order. To know in which month their birthday falls.

WHAT YOU NEED
A chart showing the months of the year in order; the register or a class list.

WHAT TO DO
Ask the children to sit in a semicircle and read out the months together. Ask them to put up their hands if they have a January birthday. Continue with each month. Check whether anyone has forgotten their birthday month, and refer to the register or a class list if necessary. Some children know the season of their birthday, or a holiday it is close to, but don't know the month.

Now say: *As we say the months, I want you to put out your legs when we say your birthday month. When we get to December, everyone should have their legs out.* It is important for self-esteem that children with a poor memory are placed next to a child whose birthday is in the same month. This will help them to remember without losing face.

DISCUSSION QUESTIONS
● *How many children have a March birthday?*
● *Who has a birthday in the last/first month of the year?*

ASSESSMENT
Do the children remember the months in sequence? Do they remember the month of their birthday?

EXTENSION
The class could work together to make a pictogram showing birthday months, and use this to answer questions.

HILL AND VALLEY MONTHS

†† Whole class
⏰ About 10 minutes

AIM
To know that different months have different numbers of days.

WHAT YOU NEED
A chart showing the months of the year in order.

WHAT TO DO
Ask the children to clench a fist and point at the knuckles with their other hand. Now ask them to look at their knuckles: *Can you see the hills and valleys? Point to a hill. Point to a valley.* Explain that you are all going to say the months of the year, touching the hills and valleys as you say each month. When you get to July, begin again.

Rehearse this several times, until the children are saying the months and touching the hills and valleys in unison. Now ask the children to say the 'hill' months loudly and whisper the valley months. Repeat, with a child pointing to the 'hill' months on the chart. Point out that all the 'hill' months have 31 days and all the 'valley' months have 30 days – except February, which is a special case.

DISCUSSION QUESTIONS
● *How many hill months are there?*
● *Are there two months next to each other with the same number of days? Are they hills or valleys?*
● *How many of you have your birthday in a 'hill' month?*
● *Is Christman in a 'hill' month or a 'valley' month?*

ASSESSMENT
Can all the children say the names of the months in order? Can they use their knuckles to show the pattern of longer and shorter months? Can they tell you which are the valley months?

EXTENSION
Print out the following rhyme (or a version of it) and learn it as a class:

Thirty days have September,
April, June and November.
All the rest have thirty-one –
Except February alone,
Which has twenty-eight days clear
And twenty-nine in each Leap Year.

TIME

SEASONS

👥 *Whole class*
🕐 *20 minutes for outside work, an hour for classroom follow-up.*

AIM
To identify the seasons by observing changes in nature. To know that the seasons have a sequence that repeats every year.

WHAT YOU NEED
A large card circle divided into quarters, labelled Spring, Summer, Autumn and Winter; a selection of collage materials such as paint, leaf prints, felt leaves, tissue flowers, twigs; access to a large flowering tree; a selection of seasonal clothes.

WHAT TO DO
Choose a significant time of the year to observe a tree near the school, for example autumn for looking at a horse chestnut tree. Ask:
● *What has happened to the leaves?*
● *What colours can you see?*
● *What else can you see under/on the tree?*
● *What are they? What are they for?*
Back in the classroom, use a quarter of the chart to make an 'Autumn' display of the tree. Ask:
● *What do you think will happen next to the tree?*
● *Which season will it be?*
Return in the winter to see whether the children's predictions were right. Check that they remember how the tree looked before. Continue through the year until each season has been represented.

Discuss seasonal weather and activities. Pictures of these could be added to the seasonal chart. Present a selection of seasonal clothes and ask the children:
● *When would you wear this? Why?*
● *Which items would you wear in summer? Why?*

DISCUSSION QUESTIONS
See above.

ASSESSMENT
Do the children understand that the environment changes in a fairly predictable way during the seasons of the year?

EXTENSION
Add the months of the year to the chart. The children can then add information about their birthday activities and relate these to the seasons (for example, you are unlikely to have a barbecue on a January birthday).

HOW MANY SLEEPS?

👥 *Whole class*
🕐 *About 10 minutes*

AIM
To calculate the number of days between two dates.

WHAT YOU NEED
A calendar, self-adhesive coloured stars, a list of significant dates for that month (birthdays, visits, holidays etc).

WHAT TO DO
Many children find it difficult to think of a number of 'days', but can easily think in terms of the number of 'sleeps' before an event. Read out the list of significant dates for that month and ask:
● *What day is it today?*
● *Who can stick a red star on today's date?*
● *When is Megan's birthday?*
● *Who can stick a blue star on the date?*
● *How many sleeps [or days] are there before Megan's birthday?*
Read out the other dates and label them on the calendar. You may want to recalculate each day, placing a new red star on the current date.

DISCUSSION QUESTIONS
● *How many sleeps before the Sports Day?*
● *Are there more sleeps before Megan's birthday or before the Sports Day? How do you know?*
● *How many sleeps will there be between the Sports Day and Megan's birthday?*

ASSESSMENT
Can the children tell you how many sleeps there are until (for example) the weekend, the school concert, the swimming day?

EXTENSION
The children can start to count in days, then in weeks and days.

A NUMBER LINE OF HOURS

†† Whole class or group
🕐 About 10 minutes

AIM
To read the time of day in hours.

WHAT YOU NEED
12 geostrips of equal length, 12 split pins, a card 'hour hand', number cards 1–12, Blu-Tack.

WHAT TO DO
Attach a number card to each split pin with Blu-tack. Use the split pins to hold 12 geostrips together in a straight line showing 1–12. Ask the children:
● *Can you count the numbers on this strip?*
● *What do you notice about these numbers?*
If necessary, explain that these are the hour numbers on a clock face. Point to various numbers and ask:
● *What time is this?*
● *How many hours are there on our strip? How much of a whole day is that? [Half.]*
● *How can I make the hour numbers into a dial like a clock face?*
● *Who can curl the strip into a dial? [They will need to place the strip on a flat surface.]*
● *Who can point to three o'clock now?*
Try other times. If the children are finding it difficult, open the dial back into a strip. As their confidence increases, put the hour hand in the middle of the dial; ask children to show you particular times, or to say times you have shown them.

DISCUSSION QUESTIONS
● *If it is three o'clock now, what time will it be in one hour? In two hours? In three hours?*
● *Can you show me using the hour hand?*

ASSESSMENT
Do the children make the connection between the strip and the dial? Can they use or read the hour hand correctly?

EXTENSION
The children can compare the geostrip dial with a clock face to see that the numbers are in the same positions.

A NUMBER LINE OF MINUTES

†† About 10 children
🕐 About 10 minutes

AIM
To understand that minutes are counted in fives on an analogue clock. **NB** The children need to be able to count in fives before attempting this activity.

WHAT YOU NEED
12 geostrips; 12 split pins; number cards showing 5, 10, 15... 60; Blu-tack; labelled card 'hour' and 'minute' hands (with the minute hand longer and thinner); a clock face. Make a long line of geostrips with the number cards attached to the pins with Blu-tack.

WHAT TO DO
Hold up the clock face. Say that we use a clock to tell the time in hours and minutes, and that the hours are the numbers on the clock face. You may want to read them together. Explain that the minutes do not have numbers, only dots: small dots for the ones and bigger dots for the fives and tens. Point these out on the clock face.

Now say that because it is so hard to follow the dots on the clock face, you have cheated and opened the dial into a straight line. Show the children the line of geostrips with the minutes labelled in fives. Ask:
● *Can you count the minutes with me?*
● *How many minutes is this? [Point to 20 minutes.]*
Curl the strip into a dial and continue finding times by counting round.

As the children become more confident, show them the hour and minute hands. Ask them to use the minute hand to show or read times on the dial. The clock can be made permanent by pinning the numbers to the dial.

DEVELOPING SHAPE, SPACE & MEASURES

DISCUSSION QUESTIONS
● *Why do we need a minute hand as well as an hour hand?*
● *How many minutes does the hand show?* [5, 10, 15 minutes.]
● *How far does the minute hand move in 30 minutes?*

ASSESSMENT
Can the children count on in fives? Can they say what the time (in minutes) will be in five minutes' time?

EXTENSION
Use cards marked 'quarter past', 'quarter to', 'half past', '25 to', '20 to', '10 to' and '5 to' in place of the appropriate number cards. You may want to do with one new card each day. The minutes 'towards' a new hour are especially difficult for young children to calculate.

HOUR AND MINUTE HANDS

†† *About 10 children*
🕐 *About 10 minutes*

AIM
To differentiate between the hour and minute hands on an analogue clock.

WHAT YOU NEED
A geared analogue clock, a real analogue clock.

WHAT TO DO
Look at the real clock and ask:
● *Can you see the hands moving round the clock?* [You will need to watch for two or three minutes.]
● *Which hand is travelling faster? [If the clock has a second hand, either explain it or ask the children to ignore it.]*
Say that it takes one minute for the minute hand to travel from one dot to the next. Ask:
● *Is the minute hand fatter or thinner than the hour hand?*
● *Is it longer or shorter than the hour hand?*
Use the geared clock to show three o'clock. Ask:
● *What time is this?*
● *Where is the hour hand pointing? [To the 3.]*
● *Where is the minute hand pointing? [To the 12.]*
● *What time will it be in one hour? [Four o'clock.]*
Try other o'clock times, asking the children to predict the time in one hour and in two hours. When they are confident, ask:
● *Can you count the minutes between four o'clock and half past four?*

● *How many minutes has the minute hand travelled?*
● *Has the hour hand travelled at all? How far?*

DISCUSSION QUESTIONS
● *How do you know where the minute hand will be at ten minutes past four?*
● *Which hand do you look at to see the minutes?*
● *How can you count the minutes?*

ASSESSMENT
Can the children differentiate between the hour and minute hands? Can they use both for telling the time?

EXTENSION
Introduce the idea of 'quarter past' the hour, then 'quarter to' the next hour. This is difficult, and (in my experience) is often better left until the first activity is firmly established.

IN ONE HOUR'S TIME

†† *About 10 children*
🕐 *About 10 minutes*

AIM
To find the time in one hour from times other than o'clock times. To understand that one hour is a complete revolution of the minute hand.

WHAT YOU NEED
A geared analogue clock for demonstration, a geared or card analogue clock for each child.

WHAT TO DO

Ask the children to find and show you four o'clock on their clocks. Check that the minute and hour hands are in the correct position. Match your clock to this, then ask:

● *What time will it be in one hour? Can you show me?*
● *Are your minute and hour hands in the correct positions?*
● *Can you all point to the hour/minute hand?*

Once the children are confident and accurate, try asking:

● *Can you find five past four?*
● *What time will it be in one hour? Can you show me?*
● *Who can show me using my clock?*
● *How far did the hour/minute hand travel?*

DISCUSSION QUESTIONS

● *How far does the hour hand travel in one hour?*
● *How far does the minute hand travel in one hour?*

ASSESSMENT

Make sure that the children can differentiate between the hour and minute hands. This is an important skill.

EXTENSIONS

● Ask the children to show you the time in half an hour.
● Ask them to tell you the time, say, 15 minutes on from five to four.

HALF AN HOUR

†† *Whole class*
🕐 *About 20 minutes*

AIMS

To understand that the minute hand travels halfway round (30 minutes) in half an hour. To count on in five-minute intervals from an o'clock time to half past.

WHAT YOU NEED

A geared analogue clock.

WHAT TO DO

Show an o'clock time and ask:

● *What time is it on the clock?*
● *Which hand tells us the hour/minute?*

Ask the children to watch as the hands turn and count aloud in fives until you get to half past, and then to shout 'STOP'. Now ask:

● *What time is it on the clock?*
● *How many minutes has the minute hand travelled?*
● *What has happened to the hour hand?*

● *What time will it be when the minute hand travels halfway round again?*
● *Where will the minute and hour hands be then?*

Ask a child to show another o'clock time on the geared clock. Encourage the child only to move the hands **clockwise**. Now ask:

● *What time is it?*
● *Which hand helps us with telling the hours?*
● *What does the long thin hand measure?*
● *What do we use to count the minutes? [The dots.]*
● *How many minutes are there between the big dots?*

Ask the children to count in fives up to half past. Go on to the next o'clock time and repeat. When they are confident, ask individual children to show times such as 20 minutes past the hour. It often helps if you ask them to show the o'clock time and then to show the minutes past, breaking the operation into two stages.

DISCUSSION QUESTIONS

● *How far has the minute hand travelled in half an hour?*
● *How many minutes is that?*

ASSESSMENT

Can the children use the hands to show minutes past the hour? Can they say where the minute hand will be at half past? Do they still differentiate clearly between the hour and minute hands?

EXTENSIONS

● The children can calculate 30 minutes from times not on the hour or half hour.
● They can start to look at times 'quarter past' the hour, then 'quarter to' the next hour.
● They can try to subtract minutes (in fives) from half past to the next hour. You may prefer to let them use 'digital' time, which is easier – for example, saying '40 minutes past three' instead of '20 minutes to four'.

TIME

DIGITAL AND ANALOGUE

♙♙ About 10 children
🕐 About 15 minutes

AIMS
To write 12-hour digital times. To relate these times to an analogue clock face.

WHAT YOU NEED
A geared clock with linked digital and analogue displays; photocopiable page 119 (one copy per child). Draw hands onto the clocks on page 119 before copying (for example, to show hours and half hours).

WHAT TO DO
Close the digital doors on the geared clock and practise telling the time. Open the digital doors. Using displays between 1:00 and 12:00, ask the children to read the times as you move the clock hands through one hour. Close the doors, display a range of analogue times and ask individual children to record the corresponding digital times on the board. Demonstrate by opening the digital doors if necessary.

Once the children are confident, give them a copy each of page 119 and ask them to record the approropriate digital times in the spaces.

DISCUSSION QUESTIONS
● *Who can write the digital time for this analogue time?*
● *What is the digital time for the analogue time 'quarter past ten'?*

ASSESSMENT
Can the children find the 12-hour digital time corresponding to a given analogue time? Can they record digital times correctly?

EXTENSION
Write digital times on copies of page 119 and ask the children to draw the corresponding analogue times.

HOW LONG DOES IT TAKE?

♙♙ About 10 children
🕐 About 15 minutes

AIM
To calculate half an hour from any time in either digital or analogue form.

WHAT YOU NEED
A geared clock with linked digital and analogue displays.

WHAT TO DO
Close the digital doors on the geared clock. Ask the children:
● *Who can show ten past six on the clock? [You may need to remind the child to find six o'clock first.]*
● *Who can write the digital time on the board? [Check the answer by opening the doors.]*
● *What time will it be in half an hour? Remember that's 30 minutes.*
● *What time will it be another half an hour after that? How do you know?*
Close the digital doors. Set a new time (eg twenty past seven). Ask:
● *Who can show the time half an hour later on the analogue clock? Remember to count in fives up to 30.*
● *What time does it show now? [7:50]*
● *Who can write the digital time on the board? [07:50]*
● *Who can read it on the analogue clock?*

DISCUSSION QUESTIONS
● *How many half-hours does it take for the minute hand to travel all the way round the clock?*
● *How many minutes are there in half an hour?*

ASSESSMENT
Can the children count on by 30 minutes? Can they read the new time from the analogue clock? Can they record it in digital form?

EXTENSIONS
● Ask the children to find the time in 20 minutes, 10 minutes or 40 minutes.
● Ask questions about real time in the classroom: *What time is it now? This activity will take 20 minutes – what time will it be at the end?* Use Blu-tack to mark the start and end times for a lesson.
● For homework, the children could use copies of photocopiable page 119 to record the starting and finishing times for three TV programmes (in both analogue and digital form) and calculate the viewing times.

MEALTIMES

†† About 10 children
🕐 About 1 hour

AIMS
To break the day into three parts: morning, afternoon and evening. To use the vocabulary 'before' and 'after'.

WHAT YOU NEED
A large zigzag book (or a display area) with the sections labelled 'before breakfast', 'breakfast', 'morning (after breakfast)', 'lunch', 'afternoon', 'tea' (or 'dinner'), 'evening'; materials for making pictures and collages.

WHAT TO DO
Read the section labels with the children. You may want to ask them to sequence the labels before starting the activity. Ask them to identify the mealtimes and to suggest appropriate food and drink for each meal. Then ask them what they might be doing during the times between meals.

The children can now prepare pictures or collages to show food or activities suitable for each section. They may want to write captions for the pictures. Finally, they should cut out their work and stick it into the appropriate sections.

DISCUSSION QUESTIONS
● *What might we eat at breakfast-time?*
● *What do you do after breakfast?*
● *Does everyone get dressed before breakfast?*

ASSESSMENT
Are the children clear about the sequence of the parts of the day?

EXTENSION
The children can make their own zigzag book to show an important day in their week, giving o'clock times for the meals.

DAY AND NIGHT

†† About 10 children
🕐 About 1 hour

AIM
To break the day into two parts: 'day' and 'night'.

WHAT YOU NEED
Two large sheets of paper, one white (labelled 'day') and one black (labelled 'night'); materials for making pictures; scissors, adhesive.

WHAT TO DO
Ask the children to read the labels. Ask for suggestions about what pictures could be shown on each sheet. You may want to compile lists of suggestions. Many children will have parents who work at night. The children could also find pictures of nocturnal animals in books – they may have a pet hamster! Let them paint 'day' and 'night' pictures. Ask them to write captions before cutting out their pictures and sticking them on the large sheets.

DISCUSSION QUESTIONS
● *Why do you think hospitals stay open at night?*
● *Do teachers teach at night? Why/why not?*

ASSESSMENT
Are the children clear about the difference between night and day?

EXTENSION
The children can use clocks to follow the hours of 'daytime' and 'night-time'. This will help them to understand that there 24 hours in a day.

JUST A MINUTE

†† About 10 children
🕐 About 10 minutes

AIM
To be aware of how long a minute is.

WHAT YOU NEED
An analogue clock with a second hand, a 1-minute sand timer (check that it measures exactly a minute).

WHAT TO DO
Show the children the clock. Ask them to watch the second hand going round. Explain that it travels round the clock once every minute. Count sixty seconds with the children. This is quite difficult, because you need to say the longer numbers faster than the slower numbers. It helps to point to the second hand as you count.

**DEVELOPING SHAPE,
SPACE & MEASURES**

Show the children the sand timer and say: *I want five children to watch the sand running through and five to watch the second hand on the clock. I want the clock children to shout 'One minute!' when the second hand has travelled round once. Are you all ready? Go!* After this activity, ask:
● *What had happened to the sand after one minute?*
● *How long did the sand take to run through?*
Swap groups and repeat. Try other activities:
● *How many times can you write your name in one minute?*
● *Did everyone write their name the same number of times?*
● *How many beads can you thread in one minute?*
● *Did everyone thread the same number?*

DISCUSSION QUESTIONS
● *Why were some children able to write their names more times than others?*
● *If you thread the beads in a pattern, do you think you will thread more or fewer in one minute?*

ASSESSMENT
Do all the children understand that the number of times they do something in one minute can vary, but the length of one minute does not?

EXTENSION
The children can try closing their eyes and estimating a minute. Discuss strategies such as counting slowly.

DINNER TIME

†† *Whole class*
🕐 *10 minutes preparation, time for meal, 15 minutes follow-up.*

AIM
To use a clock to calculate a period of time in minutes.

WHAT YOU NEED
Blu-tack, a real analogue clock, a geared analogue clock, a card clock, photocopiable page 119.

WHAT TO DO
Tell the children that they are going to find out how long it takes them to eat a meal. This could be their lunch in school or their dinner at home (if the activity is done as homework). Adapt the activity to the situation of the meal. Emphasize that the point is to record the time accurately, not finish the meal quickly!

Show them how to do it, using a real clock. Look at the clock face, agree on the time and mark it with Blu-tack. Set this time on the geared clock. Let some

time go by. Record the 'finishing time' with Blu-tack on the real clock. Record the start and finish times on a card clock, referring to the geared clock to check. Ask the children to record their own starting and finishing times on copies of page 119.

In the classroom, ask: *How many minutes did it take you to eat lunch?* It may help to divide the class by result into five-minute groups. They can use the geared clock and card clocks to count the minutes. Ask individual children to demonstrate counting the minutes.

DISCUSSION QUESTIONS
● *Who took the shortest/longest time to eat dinner?*
● *How do you count the minutes? Do you count them one by one?*
● *Which clock hand do we use to calculate the minutes?*

ASSESSMENT
Can all the children count the minutes between two marked points on a clock?

EXTENSION
Ask the children to record when they started a maths activity and when it was completed, and to calculate the time taken.

**DEVELOPING SHAPE,
SPACE & MEASURES**

NAME

DATE

CLOCK FACES

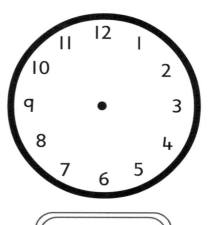

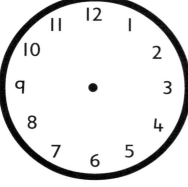

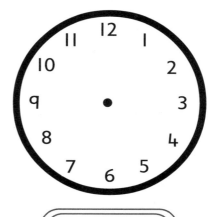

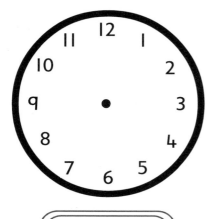

 Can you use a clock to check your answers?

SEE 'DIGITAL AND ANALOGUE' (PAGE 116), 'HOW LONG DOES IT TAKE?' (PAGE 116), 'DINNER TIME' (PAGE 118).

DEVELOPING SHAPE,
SPACE & MEASURES

NAME

DATE

OBLONGS AND SQUARES

CIRCLES AND TRIANGLES

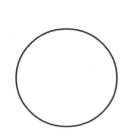
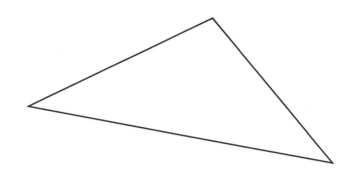
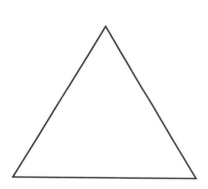
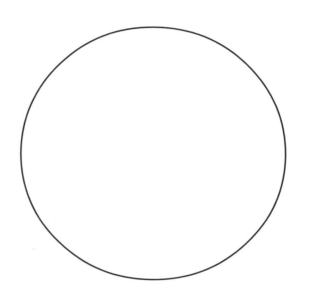
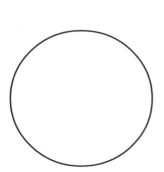
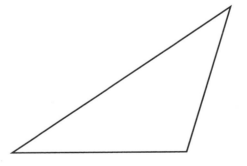

**DEVELOPING SHAPE,
SPACE & MEASURES**

PHOTOCOPIABLE

TRIANGLES

**DEVELOPING SHAPE,
SPACE & MEASURES**

OBLONGS

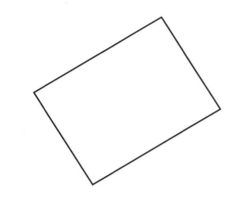

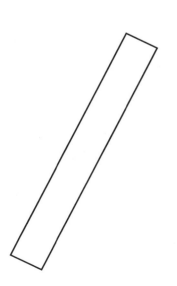

REGULAR SHAPES

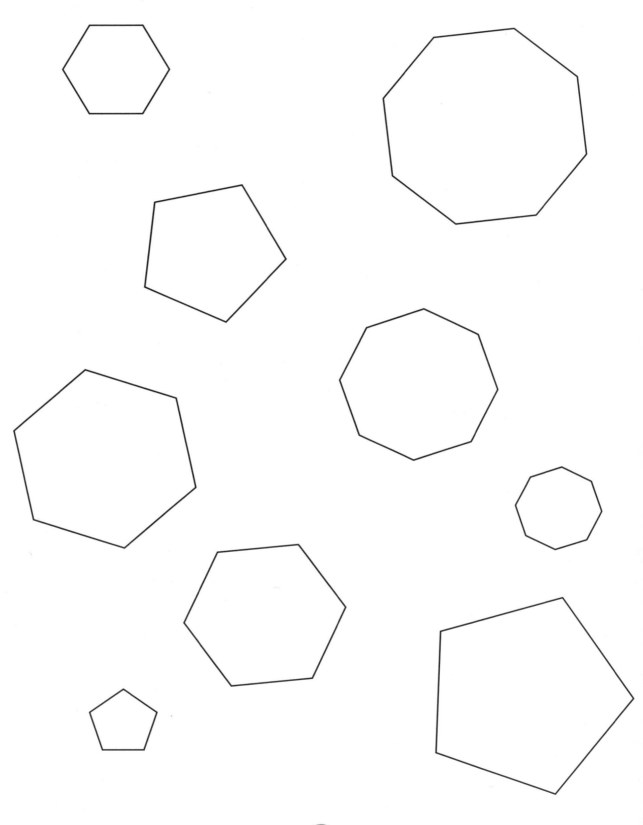

IRREGULAR SHAPES

2-D SHAPE LABELS

oblong

triangle

circle

square

pentagon

hexagon

octagon

DEVELOPING SHAPE,
SPACE & MEASURES

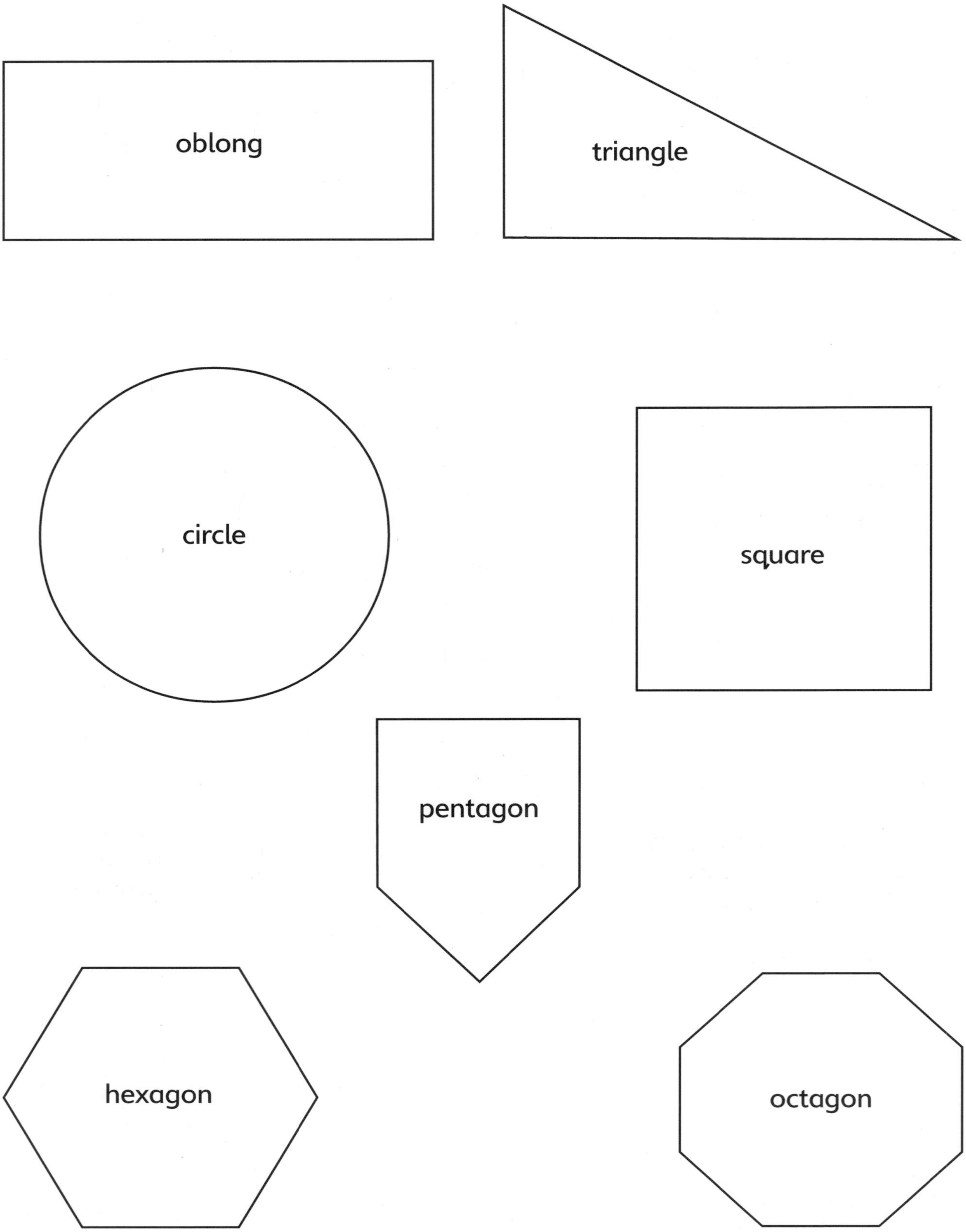

3-D SHAPE LABELS

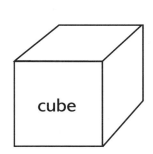

cube

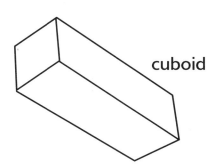

cuboid

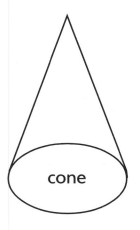

cone

cylinder

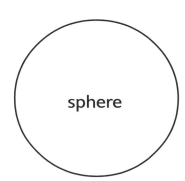

sphere

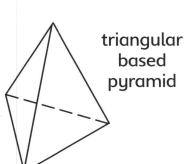

triangular based pyramid

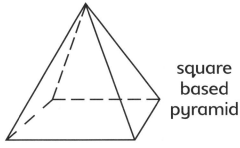

square based pyramid

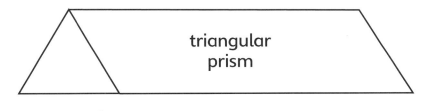

triangular prism

DEVELOPING SHAPE,
SPACE & MEASURES

WRITING FRAME

The activity was about: _____

The easy parts were:_____

They were easy because: _____

_____

How did you solve the problem? Tick a box.
Did you:

☐ ask another pupil?   ☐ use apparatus?

☐ ask an adult?   ☐ think long and hard by yourself?

Which apparatus did you use? Write or draw a picture.

Do you enjoy solving maths problems? Colour in a face.

Draw a picture of how you solved this problem. You could use a 'thinking' bubble to show how you did things in your head.

DEVELOPING SHAPE,
SPACE & MEASURES